DAN STEWART loved Kim with a passion that knew no bounds. Leaving her was the most difficult thing he would ever do—but he had no choice. He couldn't give up his children!

SUSAN STEWART couldn't face the fact that Dan had stopped loving her, so she began to drink. It wasn't a problem . . . or so she kept telling herself.

TOM HUGHES couldn't get his mind off Natalie. He knew it was ruining his marriage, but he couldn't seem to stop himself. As his attraction to his new client grew, Tom knew it was time to talk to his wife. He couldn't live a lie any longer.

———————————

Series Story Editor **Mary Ann Cooper** is America's foremost soap opera expert. She writes the nationally syndicated column *Speaking of Soaps*, is a major contributor to soap opera magazines, and has appeared on numerous radio and television talk shows.

Angelica Aimes, author of *Now and Forever*, is a celebrated romance writer. A native New Englander, she now divides her time between her Manhattan townhouse and a secluded island in the Atlantic.

Dear Friend,

One of the nicest things about serving as Story Editor for Soaps & Serials books is the opportunity to read the wonderful letters I receive from our readers. It's gratifying to know how much you enjoy these books. At Pioneer we work with the finest romance authors and editors to produce books that recapture, relish, and relive the rich history of soap operas through the retelling of stories that have entertained millions of viewers over the years.

These books bring back precious memories of the past but they raise questions too. Recently, a reader from Sheridan, Wyoming, wanted to know if the actress who was playing Lisa on AS THE WORLD TURNS was the same actress who originated the part back in the fifties. Eileen Fulton created the role of Lisa when the series premiered in 1956 and has suffered the trials and tribulations of a soap opera heroine ever since. We'll answer other reader questions in future books.

For Soaps & Serials Books,

Mary Ann Cooper

Mary Ann Cooper

P.S. If you missed previous volumes of Soaps & Serials books and can't find them in your local book source, please see the order form inserted in this book.

AS THE WORLD TURNS

7

Now and Forever

Soaps™ & Serials

PIONEER COMMUNICATIONS NETWORK, INC.

Now and Forever

AS THE WORLD TURNS paperback novels are
published and distributed by Pioneer Communications
Network, Inc.

SOAPS & SERIALS™ is a trademark of Pioneer
Communications Network, Inc.

ISBN: 0-916217-47-7

Printed in Canada

10 9 8 7 6 5 4 3 2 1

Now and Forever

Chapter One

Illusions of Love

The day was as glorious as her mood. Clear, blue skies spread over an explosion of greenery. The first crocuses were blooming in a profusion of deep purple, yellow, and white; new grass was growing all over the freshly seeded lawns of Oakdale; leaves were unfurling on the bare tree branches; magnolia blossoms were ready to burst open and the first forsythias dotted the landscape with brilliant splashes of yellow. Overnight it seemed as if winter had swept out and spring rushed in. The temperature soared to seventy degrees, a record for the last day of March in Oakdale.

Lisa stretched lazily on the canvas deck chair she'd lugged out of the garage. She couldn't remember ever feeling happier.

Looking back, it seemed as if her life had been a series of tragic mistakes and ill-conceived relationships. She'd endured three failed marriages and several impetuous affairs that had all ended in the same dismal way. But now her life was filled with hope and promise, just like the new season.

Laying aside the issue of *Vogue* she'd been reading, Lisa turned to the man stretched out on the deck chair beside hers and beamed with contentment. For the moment, Grant Coleman was unaware of her attention. All his thoughts and energies were concentrated on the heavy legal brief propped up against his knees. But Lisa didn't mind. In fact, she was pleased to find him absorbed in something other than her, because then she was free to study him as closely as she wanted. Some *thing*, not someone, she admitted to herself. If there was any other woman in Grant's life, if he even glanced at one with more than passing curiosity, she knew her jealousy would be uncontrollable. No man had ever brought her so much happiness, but no man possessed the power to cause her so much anguish.

Lisa brushed away the unpleasant thought and smiled, secure in the belief that Grant loved her as much as she loved him. At last she had everything she'd ever wished for, the wealth to indulge her every whim, two devoted sons, and now this very special man with whom to share it all. There was a look of love in her eyes as she studied him, studied the salt-and-pepper hair that showed Grant had lived and suffered, even as she had; the broad, clear brow, now furrowed in thought; the dark, deep-set eyes that burned when he looked at her with such intensity that her heart began to pound in anticipation; the firm, square jaw that revealed his fearless determination. It was a face that reflected strength and integrity, conviction and deep passion. Lisa shuddered with excitement remembering how powerful and unquenchable his passions were. Grant Coleman was one man she'd never grow tired of.

From the beginning, it seemed as though fate had brought him to her. Lisa had met Grant when she'd been lonely and terrified for her very life. She had been managing the Wade Bookstore while Penny Hughes was in England—normally a far-from-dangerous occupation. But a series of bizarre and mysterious attempts had been made on her life. Even looking back on them now, Lisa was filled with a cold, numbing dread. She'd known many men in her lifetime, and she'd incurred the fury of many jealous wives and girlfriends. Yet, until the attacks began, it had never occurred to her that anyone could hate her enough to try to murder her.

Everyone in Oakdale was talking about the case. Many blamed Lisa's notorious past. But others were suspicious of a newcomer to town, a moody, withdrawn stranger named

Jay Stallings who had taken an apartment next to the bookstore. No one knew anything about him except that he refused to divulge any information about himself and that his arrival coincided with the first attempt to kill Lisa.

Chris Hughes, an eminent attorney in Oakdale, was particularly disturbed by the attacks. Although he had long harbored bitter feelings against Lisa, he felt responsible for her safety because the Wade Bookstore belonged to his daughter, Penny. Dissatisfied with the progress the police were making, he dispatched one of the brightest lawyers in his firm to get to the bottom of the incidents. Grant Coleman was a counselor not a detective, but once he met Lisa, he knew that he would do anything to save her life—for himself.

Shaking off the old, bittersweet memories, Lisa reached over and touched the sleeve of Grant's shirt. "Have you any idea how much I love you?" she asked and smiled.

He glanced up from his brief, a look of concentration still on his face. "Are you sure it's love, darling," he teased, "and not just an excess of gratitude?"

"You mean for risking your life to save mine?"

"No risk could ever be too great to save your sweet hide," he countered, running his fingertips along her outstretched arm. "But sometimes I'm afraid you feel obliged to . . . I don't know. Repay the debt, I guess." Whenever Grant spoke, however lightly or seriously, his words always had an aura of intensity.

"Don't you think marriage is a pretty high price to pay for any debt?" she asked.

"You meant it then when you said, yes? You really do want to marry me, darling?"

"More than anything in the world," she admitted from the depths of her heart.

Grant's hand closed over hers, and he looked away. Although he was staring at the garden blooming with the first flowers of spring, he was seeing Lisa in his mind's eye. He knew every feature, every line of her body. The sky-blue eyes that glinted with irrepressible desire, the strawberry-blond hair framing the oval face, the trim, carefully maintained figure just as stunning in the designer clothes she favored as it was in nothing at all. He'd never known a more glamorous, more desirable woman.

Lisa wasn't a girl any longer, but her body was as desirable to him as a twenty-year-old's, and she was so much more worldly.

"It's a gorgeous day," he said lavishly, closing the brief and slipping it under his chair. "Much too gorgeous to waste on work."

"I think you've got spring fever, Grant Coleman," she teased.

"It's not the weather that's making me feverish. It's the beautiful woman beside me.

11

I've never seen you in the sunlight, darling," he murmured, "although you are always a garden of delights."

She answered him with a laugh that resonated with desire. "You wouldn't, Grant! Not right here on the lawn."

Slipping out of his chair, he moved confidently over to hers. "Do you really dare me?" Grant grinned. Looking as mischievous as a boy, he sat down and began to unbutton her fuchsia cotton shirt.

"What if someone comes over . . . one of the boys?" she asked weakly, a surge of desire already overwhelming any fear of discovery.

"Then we'll be caught in *flagrante*, as we lawyers like to say," he teased.

"I love you so much, darling." Her words spilled out like spring water. "I can't wait until we're married. Let's do it today, this very afternoon. I don't care about a big splashy wedding. We're both beyond the age for that. The only thing I care about is being Mrs. Grant Coleman."

Lisa felt Grant tense in her arms. "Don't you think you're being impetuous, Lisa?" he muttered darkly. But she was too filled with happiness to notice the ominous undertone in his words.

"Impetuous?" she said with a laugh. "Me? I'm not the one who just suggested making passionate love right here in the garden. Not that I can't be persuaded," she added coyly when she saw his expression change.

But it was too late to recapture the moment of free, unguarded love. With a final, almost brutal caress, Grant released her and turned away.

"What's the matter, darling?" she asked, hurt and puzzled by his abrupt rejection. "I didn't mean to pressure you. It's just that I love you so much, Grant, I'm anxious to set a date for our wedding."

Grant covered his face with his hands. His shoulders slumped and he rubbed his eyes as if he was tired of life itself. "It's not you, Lisa. It's not anything you've said or done. It's me," he confessed. "I had no right to ask you to marry me."

She stared at his hunched figure in shock and disbelief. Now just when she thought that happiness was finally in her grasp, she was suddenly filled with a cold dread. The blissful dream of a happily-ever-after marriage suddenly seemed like an illusion. "I don't understand, Grant," she said, and her voice came out like a frightened whisper, softer than the warm breeze that barely rippled the new leaves.

Lisa shivered and looked up. A great cloud had come from nowhere to hide the sun. At that moment Grant turned to her again, and it was like seeing a reflection. His face, too, was clouded like the sky.

"I haven't been aboveboard with you, Lisa. I kept hoping everything would work out, but I see now that I haven't been fair to you."

Trembling from an iciness that seemed to grip her heart, Lisa instinctively turned away from the dark, intense eyes that bored to the very depths of her being. "I love you," she murmured as if that could erase any problem.

"And I love you," he answered. "But I can't marry you, Lisa, at least not yet. I don't know how to tell you this. I know now I should have told you at the very beginning. But you just assumed I was divorced and I was so sure it would just be a formality. . . . Joyce and I haven't lived together for years."

"You mean," Lisa interrupted as his voice trailed off. "You mean you're still married to—"

"To Joyce," he concluded for her. "I never bothered to go through with divorce proceedings. It didn't seem to matter until I met you, and now Joyce is making it as difficult as she can. I don't understand why. I suppose she's still bitter and begrudges me a second chance at happiness."

"You've told her about us then?" Lisa tried to keep her voice from quavering.

"I've been begging her for a divorce since we first met." Grant's dark eyes met hers and held her as forcefully as his arms.

"You mean you knew right away?" Lisa allowed a glimmer of hope to enter her heart.

"That you were the only woman for me? Yes. Can you forgive me and be patient a little longer?" he whispered against her moist lips. The answer Lisa gave was not in words, but in the feverish desire of her mouth.

"Joyce has to agree to a divorce," he said finally when she had released him. "It's just a matter of time. Until then—"

"Until then," Lisa interrupted, "I don't know if I can help myself."

She knew the commandment, "Thou shalt not covet," but alone with Grant in a garden as lush as Eden, she yearned with all her soul to break it.

Dan Stewart ran his fingers through his mass of dark curly hair and gazed out the window, wondering for the umpteenth time if he was doing the right thing. The sky was beginning to lighten with the first gleam of morning, revealing the outlines of the cushion of clouds below. Even in this space age, flying above the clouds never failed to enchant Dan, and he glanced over at the seat beside him, eager to point out the white fluffy clouds below to his daughters. Both Betsy and Emily were still sleeping soundly, in repose their little faces as innocent and serene as those of cherubs. Tears misted his gentle brown eyes as he smiled down on them. Although he did his best to be both mother and father to his girls, he couldn't help wondering how much they had missed a woman's tender love.

Betsy had been so young when her mother

died, if it weren't for the photographs Dan kept, the little girl would have no memory of her at all. Elizabeth Talbot—sweet Liz—how he had loved her through all the turmoil their passion had created. Maybe he would tell Betsy about it sometime, when she was older. Maybe he would even explain why she was illegitimate. Dan had wanted to marry Liz, even before she became pregnant, but he wasn't free then, and Susan had stubbornly refused to give him a divorce. When she finally gave in, it was too late. Their time together had run out. He and Liz had a quiet, lovely wedding and a single perfect week. Then Liz fell, rushing down the stairs into his arms. The fall had been fatal. It was almost as if they'd been *too* happy together to survive.

Heartbroken, Dan had taken Betsy and her half sister Emily and moved to England. Liz was English and he'd wanted to give Betsy more of her mother to hold on to. Somehow, irrational though it may have been, he felt he would be closer to Liz in her own country, in the places where she had grown up and which she had loved so dearly. Then, too, his life in Oakdale had been filled with too much tragedy. He'd had to get away to put the pain behind him.

That was several years ago, and now Dan Stewart was going home. The jumbo 747 was carrying him back to Oakdale. Although he'd enjoyed England, the expatriate life wasn't for him, and he was eager to return to his own country and his own town.

Now that the sharp edges of his pain had dulled, Dan was ready to pick up the pieces of his life, even if that meant starting from square one again. Holding out his hands, he studied them critically. Although Dan knew he was a fine doctor, he didn't expect his old patients to be waiting for him. The hospital in Oakdale would take him back. He'd made sure of that before pulling up his stakes again. But he would have to build a new practice. That would mean long hours away from Betsy and Emily.

An angry frown shadowed Dan's ruggedly handsome face. He wasn't worried for Betsy. Nothing and no one could take her from him. But Emily was much more vulnerable. It was fear for her safety and her happiness that had kept him from returning to Oakdale sooner. Now even as the 747 began its final descent, he was still wondering if he had made the right move by bringing Emily back. At times he felt as if he should scoop up both his daughters and catch the next plane back to London.

The child stirred on the seat beside him, and Dan reached over to pull the thin blanket higher around her shoulders. Feeling his reassuring touch, Emily smiled in her sleep and her little hand closed tightly around his finger. Dan swallowed the lump that rose in his throat at the thought that he could possibly lose her. She looked so much like her mother. In fact, at times he thought of her as a tiny, exact replica of Susan, the same soft dark hair, huge velvet brown eyes, and small, compact body. Once upon a time, Dan had thought Susan was the only girl in the world. But that had been so long ago, long before Emily was born, long before he met Liz. As far as he was concerned, Emily had been an accident, conceived long after the love had gone out of his marriage to Susan. And yet he had never regretted her birth. In fact, he couldn't imagine life without his little Emily. She barely remembered her mother and Dan wanted to keep it that way. But once they were living in Oakdale again, would Susan insist on her rights?

Susan! Dan's expression turned grim as he thought about her. Their marriage had soured almost from the beginning. He didn't blame Susan. He was as much at fault as she. But he did fear her. He was afraid because of Emily.

Dan knew he was taking a big risk returning to Oakdale. Susan would be within her rights if she tried to gain custody of their daughter. No matter what he felt about her, Susan was Emily's mother. And he had taken the child from her—her child as well as his.

Even as the jet circled for a landing, Dan vowed to himself that he would fight Susan in every court in the country before he would give Emily up.

Chapter Two
Carefully Laid Plans

Lisa plucked the olive out of her martini with a polished nail and waited for Grant's reply. Although he'd warned her on the phone that he could only stop by for a quick drink, she was sure that once he was settled comfortably on her patio with the sun setting gloriously in the distance and a superb dinner for two cooking in the kitchen, she could persuade him to change his mind.

"I wish I could stay, darling, but I can't, not tonight." Grant stood up decisively to cut off further pleas.

"Working on a tough case?" She sipped her drink to hide her disappointment. Still she wasn't prepared to give up so easily. "I was going to make your favorite, veal scaloppine with marsala."

"It's tempting," he admitted. "But to tell the truth, I have a previous dinner engagement."

"Ohhh." She exhaled slowly, trying not to feel jealous. "Two-timing me already. Is it anyone I know?" she asked, crossing the patio and draping her arms around his neck.

"Not exactly." He planted an awkward kiss on her forehead. "It's Joyce . . . my wife," he said, plunging ahead. "She came to Oakdale to talk over our divorce."

"That's great news!" Lisa exclaimed. "If you talk together face-to-face, you're sure to work out some terms you can both live with."

"It sounds reasonable," he admitted. "But you don't know Joyce. She has a special knack for stymieing anything that she doesn't want. And she definitely doesn't want to give me a divorce."

A chill ran down Lisa's spine at his discouraging words, but she shrugged it off and smiled with forced brightness. "Don't be so negative, Grant. I'm a great believer in the power of communication. When two intelligent people sit down and talk, they can settle any question."

"They have to be reasonable as well as intelligent," Grant reminded her, "and that leaves Joyce out."

"Are you sure you're being fair to her, Grant?" Lisa asked, not for Joyce's sake, but for her own. If Grant went to dinner already convinced that nothing could be gained, then

Joyce would come out the winner without any contest. "I've never heard you sound so negative."

"Maybe you're right." He sighed, putting an arm around her and walking toward his car. "But I don't want you to get your hopes up, Lisa, at least not yet. I mean, don't go off setting a wedding date and ordering the flowers just because my wife and I are having dinner."

"Do I seem that anxious, Grant?" She forced a laugh.

"You seem perfect to me," he answered, squeezing her shoulder reassuringly. "I just like to think that you're as anxious to marry me as I am to make you Mrs. Grant Coleman."

"Lisa Coleman," she repeated, reaching up for a kiss. "It does have a certain ring to it, don't you think?"

"It's all I've been thinking about for months."

"Then don't be so glum. Joyce will have to agree," Lisa insisted. "That's all there is to it."

"I hope you're right," he murmured, taking her in his arms. For a moment he smiled down at her. "Why can't all women be like you, Lisa?"

"Because then you'd want to be a polygamist, and where would that leave me?" she retorted brightly.

They laughed as they kissed, then kissed again more deeply.

"A kiss is never enough with you, Lisa, but I have to go."

"I know." She sighed as she watched him get into the car. "It certainly won't help to keep Joyce waiting tonight."

Leaning out the window, Grant blew her a final kiss. "I'll call you tonight and tell you how it went," he promised.

"Chin up," she reminded him. "Nothing ventured nothing gained."

"You look pretty glum yourself," he said. "I hope I haven't upset you, darling."

"No, no," she assured him quickly. "It's not you, Grant. I'm a little worried about Tom, that's all. Sometimes I think he's making as much of a mess of his life as I made of mine before I met you," Lisa said softly. But she wasn't sure Grant had even heard her. He was already backing down the driveway, afraid to be late for his rendezvous with Joyce.

"Wish me luck," he called.

She watched him wave good-bye before she turned back to the house. Maybe she should call Tom and invite him and Carol over for dinner, she thought. It was a shame to waste the expensive veal she'd bought, and there was plenty for three. But once she'd called Carol, Lisa wished she hadn't. Her daughter-in-law sounded very depressed.

"Another night," she said. "But you should really check with Tom first. He's working late most of the time now. I never know when to expect him home. In fact, Lisa," she admitted, "it's been more than two weeks since I've had dinner with Tom."

"Is anything wrong, Carol?" Lisa asked anxiously.

Carol gave a short, bitter laugh. "Funny that you should ask. But I really think Tom is the one you should put that question to, don't you?"

"Maybe I will, Carol," Lisa answered thoughtfully. "Maybe I'll do just that."

Putting down the receiver, she poured herself a fresh martini and brought it out to the patio. The days were growing longer, a sure sign that summer was just around the corner. She should take a cruise to get a head start on a tan, but she didn't want to be away from Grant or Tom, at least not right now, not until her own wedding was settled and she'd had a chance to find out what was troubling her son.

Although neither Tom nor Carol had said anything to her directly, Lisa sensed that they had embarked on a rocky road, and her telephone conversation with Carol had deepened her suspicions. There was nothing Lisa hated more than an interfering mother-in-law. Still she made up her mind to have a heart-to-heart talk with Tom.

Admittedly she hadn't been much of a mother to him. More times than she liked to remember, she'd walked out on him, leaving his grandmother to bring up the boy as best she could. The insecurity of his early years had been too much for him. He'd been a difficult child and a troubled adolescent. Then he'd gone to Vietnam and come home suffering, traumatized by a terrible war experience. For a time it seemed as though he would be permanently damaged, an emotional, psychological casualty of the war. Looking back, Lisa still felt the agony and the guilt. Those were the worst times for mother and son.

The nightmare days came back to Lisa as vividly as if she were living through them again. In Vietnam Tom had become hooked on drugs. Back home he was caught stealing them from Dr. Michael Shea's medical cabinet. Michael had been Lisa's lover at the time, a mistake she'd recognized too late, one of the countless mistakes about men she'd made in her lifetime. When Michael was found murdered, Tom had been arrested and put on trial.

Desperate to save her son, Lisa began to investigate the case herself. She knew Tom had problems, yet her heart told her that he was not a killer. Tom was innocent. Someone else was the real murderer, and Lisa was determined to find out who it was. She couldn't sit by and allow her son to rot in jail.

Taking a long drink of her martini, she remembered how she'd studied the case night and day, until finally she'd discovered that the true murderer was one of Michael's old girlfriends. Free at last, Tom drew closer to his mother than he had ever been. And for her part, Lisa tried to make up to him for all the years of neglect. But it wasn't easy for either of them.

Tom wasn't used to having his mother interfering in his life. Yet Lisa had made so many mistakes herself, she couldn't sit by quietly and watch her son make the wrong choices, especially when it came to marriage. Lisa had wanted him to marry Carol. She was such a sweet, warm girl, and she was crazy about him. But Tom had been infatuated with wealthy, rebellious Meredith Halliday. When nothing Lisa said could convince her son that he was making a terrible mistake, she took the matter into her own hands, conniving behind Tom's back to get Meredith out of Oakdale.

Lisa had gotten her way as she usually did. Tom had married Carol, and everything was exactly the way Lisa had planned. But increasingly, she had the ominous feeling that her son's marriage wasn't working out. Something was wrong, but she didn't know what.

Late that night when Grant finally called, she was still brooding over her son and daughter-in-law.

"How did it go, darling?" she asked eagerly. But the tone of his voice alone gave her the answer she didn't want to hear.

"Just as I knew it would," he replied glumly. "When it comes to divorce, Joyce won't give an inch."

"But she has to," Lisa insisted. "I want to marry you, Grant."

"What can I say?" he answered, too tired from arguing all evening with Joyce to get into a pointless discussion with Lisa. "I'll keep pressing her, but it's like banging my head against a brick wall."

"But, darling . . ." Lisa felt like crying.

"I'll call you in the morning and give you all the gory details," he interrupted. "But right now I'm going to get some sleep. I'm beat, and I've got a long day ahead of me tomorrow."

"I'm sorry, Grant," she said contritely. "One irate woman a night is enough for any man. Sleep tight."

Hanging up the phone, she wandered restlessly through the house. Although it was past midnight, she hadn't gotten around to eating her own dinner. But Lisa had no appetite for food. None of her carefully laid plans were working out, not her plans for Tom and Carol, and certainly not her plans for Grant.

The hospital cafeteria was nearly deserted as Dr. Dixon entered, balancing a cheese Danish on top of the stack of charts he carried. Picking up his mug of coffee, he looked for a place to sit. He didn't feel like being alone that morning, but at first glance it seemed he had no choice. Wednesdays were always the quietest days at the hospital, the doctors' traditional day off. A group of nurses on their mid-morning break were crowded at a single table in the center of the long room. A couple of exhausted interns were gulping black coffee at a corner table. Dr. Dixon didn't want to join either group. Then he saw a woman sitting by herself at the far end of the cafeteria, and a thin smile creased his lips. Probably she had chosen that precise location to discourage any company, he thought as he headed directly for her table.

"Good morning, Susan. I didn't expect to find you here this morning." Dr. Dixon put his coffee beside hers and sat down without waiting for an invitation.

Irritation at this unwanted intrusion was marked clearly on Dr. Susan Stewart's face as she looked up at him. It was just like John Dixon to join her whether he was welcome or not. He acted as if he owned the Memorial Hospital, she thought resentfully. "Morning John," she answered curtly. "I was just finishing."

"No need to rush back," he said amiably. "The research lab can function a few more minutes without you, I'm sure."

"I didn't mean to suggest that I'm indispensable," she snapped back.

Dr. Dixon grinned slyly. "If I didn't know better, I'd think you got up on the wrong side of the bed this morning. But seriously, Susan, I don't blame you for being out of sorts today. I know it will be a little awkward for you, at least at first. But the hospital board really had no choice. Good doctors aren't that easy to come by these days, and we are dangerously understaffed."

"Awkward? What are you talking about, John?" Susan demanded, putting her empty tray down again and fixing him with a sharp, unswerving stare.

He met her gaze with a bland, innocent expression. "About Dan coming back on staff. What else could you think?"

"Dan's in England," she retorted sharply. "You know that as well as I do. So what kind of games are you trying to play with me, John?"

"Dan *was* in England. I can't believe you haven't heard the news. I would have thought you'd be the first one. . . ." His voice trailed off in surprise, genuine or otherwise, she couldn't be sure. "Well, anyway, he wrote requesting to be reinstated, and the administration agreed. He's due to report next week. Dan's a first-rate doctor, and we can use him around here," he added more gently.

Susan's face had paled so alarmingly he wished he'd held his tongue for once. "Are you all right?" he asked, squeezing her hand reassuringly. It was ice-cold beneath his touch.

Forcing herself to keep calm, Susan pulled away from his touch. "Fine. Why wouldn't I be?" she lied in a voice that dared him to challenge her.

"I'm sorry. I thought you knew or I wouldn't have said anything."

She cut off his apology. "Since you're so full of news, you can tell me this," she said acidly. "Is Dan coming back alone?"

Dr. Dixon hesitated. Everyone in Oakdale knew about the ugly marital triangle that finally split up Susan's marriage, as well as about Liz Talbot's tragic, unexpected death just days after her wedding to Dan. Was Susan really expecting her former husband to come back to Oakdale bringing another English wife home with him? "I really don't have any details," he answered. "Dan has bought a house big enough for himself and the girls from the sound of it."

Although Dr. Dixon went on talking, Susan didn't hear him. She was totally oblivious to her surroundings. Finally she managed to say, "Dan is coming back, and he's bringing Emily with him."

She spoke aloud but it was clear she was talking to herself. Her large brown eyes stared at John Dixon without really seeing him. She'd spent so many long, lonely hours imagining the moment when Dan would return. Now that it was at hand, she couldn't believe it. Her heart was a tangle of wild, confused emotions. At that instant all she knew clearly was that she had to get away from John Dixon. She had to be alone.

Pushing back her chair, she muttered distractedly, "I'm sorry. I've got to get back, John. I'll talk to you later." Before he could stop her, she darted away.

Dr. Dixon watched until her slender figure reached the cafeteria door, then he turned back and bit into his cheese Danish, wondering if Dan Stewart knew just how much unfinished business he was coming back to. Susan's reaction had made it clear. In spite of their divorce, she clearly hadn't put her former husband out of her life. Women were so complicated and so devious. Chewing thoughtfully, he tried to decide exactly what was on Susan's mind: Dan Stewart or her daughter Emily.

Back in the research lab, Susan pulled her white coat around her and hugged herself although the room was warm.

"Are you feeling all right, Doctor?" her young lab assistant asked anxiously when he saw her ashen face.

"Just a slight headache . . . nothing to worry about," she reassured him with a forced smile. "Why don't you take your break now."

"I was just finishing up this test," he began to protest.

"It can wait until you've had a cup of coffee," she cut in.

"Well if you're sure. . . ."

"Quite sure," she said sharply and turned away. Such dedication was admirable sometimes. Other times, it was downright annoying.

Alone at last, Susan wandered around the research lab, clenching her hands to keep them from trembling. John Dixon couldn't be lying, yet it seemed so unreal, like a dream, a fantasy. Dan was really coming home at last and there was no Liz Talbot around anymore to get in her way. In spite of their stormy, often bitter marriage, Susan had never stopped loving Dan, never stopped dreaming that one day he'd return. And now he was. Maybe he was in Oakdale already, she thought. Her heart raced at the possibility.

Dan! She closed her eyes tightly and saw his face before her, more handsome than any man's in Oakdale. The rugged features, the warm, smiling eyes, the deeply cleft chin, the thick dark curls that she'd loved to run her fingers through when she lay by his side. Hugging herself tighter, she felt his arms around her again as they'd been at the beginning. Dan had been so full of desire he couldn't keep from touching her. What had happened to them? What had she done wrong?

Tears filled her eyes, but she blinked them away angrily. She and Dan would still be happily married if Liz Talbot had not insinuated her way into their lives with her upper-class British ways and oh-so-charming manners. Dan had been infatuated by everything about Liz, but Susan had seen through her right away. Liz was nothing but a conniver and a liar, Susan remembered. Time, even death, had done nothing to ease her bitterness. Had it changed the way Dan felt? Susan could only hope.

She stopped at the window and gazed out over the sea of automobile roofs that filled the hospital parking lot. The day was overcast, the threat of rain clear in the sky, but the weather had not deterred scores of relatives and friends from flocking to the early visiting hours. Susan stared out without seeing, too overwhelmed by the conflicting emotions swirling within her. She'd done everything to hold on to Dan once. She'd lied, tricked, plotted, even gotten pregnant to keep him from leaving her. But he'd gone anyway, taking her baby away too. Emily would be four, by now. She wouldn't even remember her mother. Yet that hardly mattered to Susan. The child belonged to her and Dan together.

As she turned away from the window, her mind was racing with the new possibilities that were suddenly opening to her. The color had returned to her face, flushing her cheeks with suppressed excitement. The shock at hearing of Dan's arrival had passed, and Susan was already beginning to plan a new life for herself and her husband.

At first, she'd try to win Dan back purely by the force of her love. She did love him still, no matter what he believed. But if that failed, there was always Emily. Susan nervously fingered a beaker on the long lab table. She didn't know her daughter. She didn't know what kind of a mother she would be. Her work was so important to her. Still she was prepared, if she had to, to sue Dan for custody of the child.

Susan was sure she'd win. The courts always favored the mother, and Dan had stolen the child from her and taken her to another country, another continent. She smiled in secret triumph. If Dan wanted to keep her out of his life, he was making a mistake coming back to Oakdale. One way or another, he was going to have to see her again . . . and again . . . and again. Susan would make sure of that. And once she was back in his life, without the threat of Liz Talbot to come between them, anything could happen.

By the time her assistant got back from his break, Dr. Susan Stewart was already weaving her hopes and dreams and private ploys into a glorious future. She and Dan would have a second wedding, a spectacular celebration. They'd invite the whole of Oakdale, and little Emily would be their flower girl.

Chapter Three
Accidents Will Happen

"Grant, it's for you, darling." Lisa held out the receiver for him, thrillingly aware of the hand that had slunk under the sheet while she answered and, at that very moment, was burning its way up her thigh.

"Too busy to talk to anyone now," he murmured huskily, his hand sliding dangerously higher. "I'm on a secret mission—very delicate, very explosive."

"No, darling, not now," Lisa whispered urgently, moving away from him. In another second, she wouldn't be able to say no. "It's John Dixon. He says it's an emergency."

"Dixon?" Grant pulled away abruptly and sat up. "What does he want with me at this hour?"

Frowning, he took the receiver and grunted, "Grant Coleman."

Lisa lay back and waited, the desire that his touch had aroused fading as she watched the frown on his face deepen. John Dixon wouldn't be calling her house looking for Grant at two o'clock in the morning if it weren't some kind of medical emergency. But what could it be? An injured client? Grant had no family to speak of—except . . .

Before Lisa had time to put her thought into words, Grant was leaning across her to jam the receiver down on the cradle.

"Damn it," he growled. "If I didn't know it was à medical impossibility, I'd swear she did it to herself, and at this precise moment."

"Your wife?" Lisa closed her eyes, tired and already disgusted.

"My ex-wife," he corrected angrily. "Damned if I know how Dixon knew I was here."

"It's not exactly a well-kept secret," she answered, opening one eye to glare at him sarcastically, "that you and I are keeping company. In fact, with my back against the wall, I doubt if I could name two people in Oakdale who don't know that we're sleeping together. What's the matter with dear Joyce, anyway?"

"Dear Joyce," he repeated, suddenly feeling very tired of the whole impossible situation, "has just been rushed to the hospital with a ruptured appendix. Dr. Dixon felt that, as the next of kin, I should be informed immediately. Joyce is on her way into surgery now. Depending on how acute a case it is, a ruptured appendix can be critical."

"I'm sorry, Grant." Lisa sat up, stunned by the unexpected news. "I can't say I've been thinking kindly of Joyce lately, but I don't wish her dead." She shivered and pulled the sheet high around her shoulders. All at once she felt cold. "I guess you'd better get over to the hospital right away."

"Are you sure you don't mind?" His gaze seemed to bore into her, searching for the truth.

"How could I, Grant? She is your wife and she's desperately sick." Slipping out of bed, she reached for her bathrobe and wrapped it tightly around her. "I don't want you to go—I never want you to go—but under the circumstances . . ."

Grant had gotten up while she spoke and was already pulling on his trousers. "You don't resent my running out on you like this?"

"Don't worry about me, darling." Lisa came around the bed and reached up to knot Grant's tie.

"You wanted to make love tonight. You were so ready when I touched you."

"There'll be other nights, a whole lifetime of nights together." She smiled up at him.

Grant shook his head as if he could no longer believe her words. Lisa didn't know Joyce the way he did. She would do almost anything to keep his divorce from going through. "If I didn't know it was impossible, I'd stake my life that Joyce planned this whole attack," he muttered, a frown creasing his face.

"Don't be ridiculous, Grant," Lisa said, trying to laugh.

"I wouldn't put it past her. I wouldn't put anything past her. You don't know that woman the way I do."

Turning away, Lisa walked to the window and drew back the curtain. The night was black and clear, the stars, sharp pinpoints gleaming in the sky. "What are you trying to tell me, Grant?" she asked in an emotionless voice.

"Just that this . . . this accident, or whatever it was, puts everything on hold, at least until Joyce is out of the woods." He came up behind her and wrapped his arms around her waist, pulling her against him.

Lisa closed her eyes and forced herself to speak evenly. "You mean our wedding is off again."

"Not off," he said and sighed, "just delayed again. I can't very well press Joyce for the divorce when she's in intensive care."

Put that way it did sound heartless, and yet maybe if he pressed her while she was at her weakest. . . . Lisa pushed the vicious thought away. She might do it herself, but she could never ask Grant to. What would he think of her if she did? She hoped he'd never discover the awful things she had done before she'd met him. With a deep sigh she turned in his arms. "Do whatever you think is best, darling," she assured him. "I've waited this long for you, I guess I can wait a little longer."

"Have I ever told you how wonderful you are, Lisa?" Grant asked, hugging her against him.

"Once or twice, but I don't mind repetition," she murmured, molding her body against his.

"Neither do I," Grant whispered against her mouth, "especially this kind of repetition," he added, kissing her lips again and again.

With each kiss his lips lingered on hers a little longer, until finally they were locked together in an embrace that fused them body and soul. Grant's hands slid beneath her robe, caressing her smooth skin. She knew that in another second she wouldn't be able to let him go—no matter what Joyce's condition was.

Though still trembling from the thrill of his touch, Lisa forced herself to break away. "You'd better go now, Grant," she insisted. "Because if you don't, there's going to be an emergency right here."

"Mmmm," he murmured. "I can think of a thousand ways I'd like to treat it."

"Well, don't tell me about them," she warned. "I don't want to lie here all night alone, imagining how divine your treatments would be."

Grant kissed her one last time, reluctant to let go of her. "Tomorrow night," he promised, walking her with him to the bedroom door, "I won't give you any rest."

Lisa watched him disappear down the hall, and still she stood at the door, listening to his footsteps on the stairs, the flat thud of the front door shutting, the sudden roar of the car engine echoing through the open window.

Alone, she lay down on the bed and inhaled deeply. Grant's special scent, a mingling of lime aftershave and his own unique, intensely virile odor, clung to the sheets. Burying her face in them, she felt the last trace of desire give way to anger.

"Damn you, Joyce Coleman," she swore softly. "I won't let you keep Grant. No matter what you do, I'm going to have him. No matter how you try to stop us, I'm going to be Mrs. Grant Coleman."

"Carol!" Jay Stallings leaned over to the passenger seat of his gleaming new silver-gray Porsche and stuck his head out. "Carol, over here!"

Bewildered, the slender girl looked around her for a moment. Her arms were so filled with packages she could barely see where she was going. Then she caught sight of the Porsche parked in the middle of a bus stop, and a bright smile warmed her blue eyes. Flicking back her shoulder-length red hair, she readjusted the packages in her arms and walked over.

"Jay, what are you doing here?" she asked when she reached the car.

"Just happened to be in the neighborhood," he lied, pushing the door open for her. "Hop in and I'll give you a lift."

Carol Hughes shook her head, every feature of her bright, pretty face registering amazement. "I don't know what it is about you, Jay," she admitted incredulously. "You just always seem to be in the right place at the right time . . . at least for me," she added, sinking back into the rich leather seat with a satisfied sigh.

"Coincidence," he lied again. "Or just lucky." He smiled, happy that she didn't suspect how often he had followed her in the last month, tailing her as closely as he dared and then pretending to bump into her. It was the only way he could think of to get to see her often because Carol Hughes was not the kind of wife to cheat on her husband—even if he deserved it.

"I'm the lucky one, today," she admitted. "I must be crazy. I never stopped to think how I was going to get all these packages home."

"Looks like you bought out every store in Oakdale," he said with a laugh, glancing at the mound of packages which filled the back of the car.

"I guess I did overdo it a little," she admitted, blushing with embarrassment. "I don't even like to shop much. I mean I'm not one of those women who loves to go from store to store looking at everything and trying things on. But this time I went on a real binge." The color drained from her face, and the brightness seemed to fade from her eyes. "The worst of it is, I'm sure none of this is going to help at all."

"What do you mean, Carol? I'm not sure I understand what you're getting at."

"Nothing really. At least nothing that I want to drag you into." She touched his arm as if for reassurance. "You're a good friend, but I'm sure you've got your own problems."

Jay paused, his hand gripping the stick shift tightly, and studied her. "You can talk to me, Carol. You can trust me. That's what friends are for, you know."

"It's not the kind of thing I can talk about." She hesitated. "It's something between Tom and me, something we've got to work out ourselves."

"Okay, if that's the way you want it. Believe me, Carol, I'm not trying to butt in between you and your husband," Jay snapped. His eyes flashed angrily and he gunned the engine, speeding away before the driver of the bus that was just pulling up behind him had a chance to lean on his horn.

Carol was naive, almost to the point of being innocent. It was one of the qualities Jay found most appealing about her. But at the same time, it was occasionally frustrating.

Could she really believe that all the chance meetings he so carefully planned were blind luck? Didn't she have any idea that the friendship he offered her was just an excuse to be with her without arousing her husband's suspicions? Jay didn't want to help her save her marriage to Tom Hughes. That was the last thing in the world on his mind. He wanted to destroy it. But first he must persuade Carol to confide in him.

Stroking his moustache thoughtfully, he glanced at her just in time to see a solitary tear rolling down her cheek. His expression softened, and he reached over and caught it with the back of his finger. "Hey, what's this?" he asked gently. "Didn't I tell you the rules when I picked you up? No crying allowed in this Porsche."

Carol tried to smile, but Jay's kindness at that moment was more than she could bear. "I'm sorry," she whispered, "but I can't help myself."

"Then let me help you," he murmured, pulling onto a quiet street shaded with huge maples and oaks. Turning off the ignition, he took her in his arms. "There," he said softly, holding her securely, "now you can cry as much as you want to, and you don't have to be afraid, baby. I'll be right here beside you whenever you need me."

"I don't know what I'd do without you, Jay," she said, sobbing against his chest. "I'm so confused . . . so unsure."

"Why don't you begin at the beginning and tell me all about it." He stroked her long, shimmering hair. It was as red as a fiery sunset. Threading his fingers through it, just as he had often dreamed of doing, he let his fantasies run wild for a moment. Carol needed more than a shoulder to cry on, and Jay Stallings was more than eager to provide it.

"It's Tom," she admitted, burrowing her face deeper into his chest. "Oh, Jay, I don't know what to do or what to think. I love him, and I know I should trust him. But I can't, at least not where Natalie Bannon is concerned." A fresh burst of sobs shook her slender frame.

"I'm sure this Natalie isn't half as warm and loving and wonderful as you are," Jay assured her, hugging her closer.

"I wish Tom thought that." Carol glanced up, her pain apparent in her eyes.

"How do you know he doesn't?" Jay asked shrewdly as his hands rubbed her back soothingly, subtly easing her inhibitions.

"Because he spends all his time with Natalie. I hardly ever see him anymore," she cried. "Tom insists Natalie is just a new client, but he has other new clients who aren't beautiful, young, and very available and he isn't working nights and weekends with them," she added bitterly.

"Have you talked to Tom and told him how you feel?" Although Jay was careful to sound concerned and helpful, inside he was scheming. He didn't care what Tom Hughes's relationship with Natalie was. His only concern was to make Carol believe absolutely that they were lovers. If she was convinced she'd lost her husband, anything could happen, Jay thought.

"I've tried." Carol sniffled like a hurt child. "But he won't talk about it. He just brushes aside my questions. He keeps saying if I loved him, I'd trust him. . . ." Her voice trailed off. "And I know that's true," she added dejectedly. "I'm so mixed up, Jay. I don't know what I feel or what I think anymore. I'm afraid I've lost Tom. When I started out this morning I felt so sure I could win him back if I made myself more . . . more attractive."

"You're already very, very attractive just the way you are."

"I guess I'm pretty enough in a wholesome kind of way. But I thought if I could make myself glamorous, sophisticated like Natalie . . ."

"That's what all these boxes and bundles are?"

Carol nodded.

"A man doesn't love a woman for the clothes she wears," Jay said. "You must know that."

"I know it was dumb of me. But I'm so desperate. What should I do, Jay? Help me. Please, help me!" She clung to him as if he was her last hope, and he felt the urgent beating of her heart against his own.

Tilting her chin so that her face was turned up to his, he gazed at her longingly. "For starters," he murmured, his voice low and taut with emotion, "you have to believe that you're more beautiful, more desirable than any other woman in Oakdale."

"How can I believe that when I know. . . ." she began. But something in his face, something in his eyes stopped her.

"Because I'm going to show you that you are, Carol," he whispered. His fingertips grazed her neck and cheek as lightly as a summer breeze and his lips reached down to touch hers, gently at first, then more insistently.

At first Carol felt as if she'd been paralyzed by his touch, she was so surprised. Yet she didn't pull away. She held her lips motionless against his, but gradually, her body responded instinctively, hungrily. For a long time now Tom's touch had elicited only resentment and mistrust from Carol. She couldn't help but wonder if he held Natalie the same way he held her, if he kissed her the same way, made love to her the same way. Carol was so suspicious that she could no longer find happiness in Tom's arms. Starved for affection, for caring, for the intimacy that she'd once shared with her husband, Carol began to surrender to Jay's kiss. Against her will, her lips opened to the moist warmth of his tongue. She couldn't retreat. Her mind struggled to be free of the irresistible power of his embrace, but her body behaved like a wild rebel.

Jay had hoped to steal a quick kiss. Instead he had awakened a desperate passion. Not even in his dreams had he imagined that Carol would be so willing. Crushing her in his arms, he delved deeper and deeper into the warm recess of her mouth. His lips burned with desire to possess her wholly and completely, to make her his own as Tom Hughes never had.

Then just when he thought Carol would be his, she broke away, her face flushed a deep crimson, her body still trembling with the force of their kiss.

"Oh, God!" she exclaimed. "What are we doing? What am *I* doing? I'm a married woman. I've never. . . ." Carol shook her head in confusion and despair.

For a brief moment, Jay stared at her hungrily. He was intensely aware of everything about her, the way her breath still came in short, quick gasps, and her lips still quivered from the power of their kiss. "I told you I was going to show you how desirable you are," he whispered. "I always keep my promises, Carol. Always."

Carol turned away, as shaken by his words as she was by his kiss. Tom was her husband, and she loved him. She'd never questioned that before. Yet if she really did, how could she have responded so easily and so completely to another man? Jay was nothing more than a friend. Or was he? She sank back against the seat feeling frightened and unsure of herself, her marriage, and the man beside her. "I—I think I should go home, Jay," she managed to stammer.

With a final burning glance at her, Jay revved the engine and pulled back onto the main road. They drove the rest of the way in a tense silence, each one acutely conscious of the other and the moment of unexpected passion they had just shared.

"If there's anything you need or want, Carol—" he began when he stopped in front of her house.

"Nothing." She cut him off more sharply than she'd intended.

He reached for her hand and held it before she could open the door. "Forgive me, baby," he said contritely. "I know I went too far but believe me, I was only trying to help you."

"Are you sure that's all it was?" she asked looking up at him with wide questioning eyes. Oddly, his words had stung her more than she dared admit even to herself.

He met her gaze squarely. "I do want to help you because I want you to be happy, but I wanted to kiss you, too. I'd be lying if I denied that, and I don't want to lie to you, Carol. It looks like your husband does enough of that."

Carol seemed to jerk back at his words as if

he'd struck her. "Then you believe that Tom's cheating on me, too?" she challenged.

"Hold on a minute." He put up his hands defensively. "Don't put me in a position of accusing your husband. I have no way of knowing what he's doing or feeling. All I know is that when a man stays out night after night with the same beautiful client, it's hard to keep his mind on his work."

"Is that the way you are too?" Her voice caught with a stifled sob.

"If I were married to you, Carol, I don't think I'd remember that there were any other women in the world."

She shook her head, not wanting to believe him. "That's what you say now, Jay."

"That's what I would say forever, if the kiss you just gave me is any indication of what you feel in your heart." Reaching over, he brushed her cheek with his fingers. "If," he murmured. "The best dreams are made of ifs."

Chapter Four
The Price Of Love

"Do you really think it was a good idea, John?" Kim Dixon admired her reflection in the oval mirror as she fitted a pair of diamond studs in her pierced ears.

"You mean inviting both Dan and Susan tonight? We didn't really have a choice. Considering my position, I had to have some sort of affair to welcome one of the hospital's foremost surgeons back on the staff. And Susan is a good friend. What should I have done, invite all the other doctors and leave her out?"

Kim leaned closer to the vanity mirror to check her eyeliner and looked sharply at her husband's reflection mirrored there. "Are you sure that's the only reason, John?"

"What do you mean? What devious, ulterior motives are you accusing me of now?"

"Oh, nothing really." She laughed lightly. "It just occurred to me while I was soaking in the tub that Susan Stewart might have put you up to staging this whole affair."

"Why would she do that?"

"Why?" She threw an incredulous glance over her shoulder at him. "Because she wants to get Dan back and, if the Oakdale grapevine is as reliable as usual, he's been avoiding her like the plague ever since he got home."

Through the mirror, Kim saw her husband do a quick double take and knew her hunch was right. Susan *had* put John up to throwing a cocktail party, supposedly in Dan's honor, but actually to serve her own devious motives. Kim had never trusted Susan, and sometimes she wasn't sure that she should trust John either.

Coming up behind her, he rested his chin on her shoulder, inhaling the intoxicating scent of her perfume. "I never realized I had such a suspicious wife," he said teasingly. His fingers moved hungrily along the bare, smooth skin of her back, but with a light peck on his cheek, she twisted free of his embrace.

"I've got to check on the hors d'oeuvres. Your guests will be arriving any minute."

"You never used to pull away from me, Kim," he said accusingly.

"You never used to keep secrets from me," she countered. "Really, John, don't you and

Susan think I'm old enough to be let in on your little plots?"

"I don't want to talk about Susan. I want to talk about us. You look stunning, Kim," he said almost wistfully, allowing his eyes to linger along the length of her body, so subtly yet superbly displayed by her black crepe sheath. Cut high in the front, it plunged to a deep V in the back, and the slender lines hugged her figure, outlining every contour to perfection. "The perfect hostess."

"I just hope," she said, arching a carefully penciled eyebrow, "that the perfect hostess doesn't find herself presiding over a perfect catastrophe."

"Don't worry." John laughed. "Susan and Dan are both consenting adults."

"Dan, yes. But I have my doubts about your girlfriend," she retorted.

"Susan has promised to be on her best behavior."

Kim shot a skeptical look at her husband but decided to hold her tongue. There was no point in arguing over Susan Stewart now. Like it or not, she was coming to the party. Still, Kim couldn't shake off the feeling of resentment that had been nagging at her all afternoon. It would have been so easy for John to level with her at the outset and say that he wanted to give a party to bring Dan and Susan Stewart back together. Am I so formidable, so unapproachable that my own husband is afraid to tell me the truth? Kim wondered as she glided through the rooms, plumping a pillow on the sofa, shining a glass at the bar, rearranging a spray of cherry blossoms. She dismissed the thought with a shrug. She wasn't the one at fault. It was John.

There had been a time when she thought Dr. John Dixon was the most brilliant, dynamic, intrepid man she'd ever met. But marriage had lifted the blinders. Her disillusionment had been gradual but complete. John was an able doctor, but as a husband and a man, he was insecure. She never doubted his love but she questioned his strength. Instead of freeing her to respond with her whole heart, his devotion was like an iron chain holding her back. He needed her too much. It was suffocating.

The doorbell chimed, interrupting Kim's thoughts. As the guests began arriving, she automatically put her own dissatisfactions on hold, but as the evening lengthened and she found herself engaged in an intense conversation with the guest of honor, they returned with even greater force.

With a stab of guilt for being disloyal, Kim found herself measuring Dan Stewart against her husband. Although she knew it was unfair, she couldn't help comparing the two doctors. Looking at Dan's lean, athletic body, at his dark hair and cleft chin, delighting in the humor reflected in his eyes and the contagious warmth of his smile, Kim wondered how any woman could let him go. No wonder Susan Stewart was so determined to win him back.

Still Kim had never been attracted by physical appearance alone. The man's personality was much more important to her. Yet here too, Dan came out the clear winner. He was strong, direct, sure of himself. He seemed to be everything her own husband was not.

As if he could read his wife's thoughts, John Dixon came up beside her and slipped a possessive arm around her waist. "If I didn't know you better, Dan, I'd be jealous," he said. "You've been monopolizing my wife all evening."

"The guest of honor's prerogative." Dan grinned innocently. "Anyway, you can't blame me, John. Your wife happens to be the most beautiful woman in the room."

"Flattery, flattery," Kim said and laughed but she couldn't control the deep flush that rose to color her cheeks.

"I can't disagree with you on that point," John admitted readily, "but there is someone else at the party who's very anxious to see you and mend fences."

Before he could reply, Susan Stewart appeared as if on some predetermined cue from John. She looked pale and nervous, though pretty enough, Kim thought grudgingly, in a turquoise jacquard silk dress.

Wedging herself between the two men, Susan said almost shyly, "Hello, Dan. It's been a long time."

Dan's face froze in a hard, unyielding mask when he found himself trapped. Obviously he had no idea that his former wife would be at the party, too, Kim thought as she moved out of the circle of her husband's arm. It was a dirty trick to set Dan up like this, she realized angrily. John should have warned him beforehand.

Dan stared at the three of them coldly as if they were all coconspirators. "Yes, it has been a long time," he admitted stiffly, "long enough for you to make a new life for yourself just as I have, Susan. That's why I'm very surprised to see you here tonight." His voice, like his eyes, held all the warmth of a glacier.

"You understand, Dan," John began with forced bravado, "we invited everyone on the staff without exception, didn't we, sweetheart?" He turned to Kim for support and was met with a withering glare.

"I kind of thought you would call when you got home, Dan," Susan said tentatively. "I mean knowing how much I have missed my baby. How is Emily?"

He fixed her with a look as unyielding as granite. "Your maternal feelings are emerging four years too late, don't you think, Susan? You never wanted Emily. Having her was just a ploy to keep me, but all that is ancient history, and I intend to keep it that way.

Emily is very happy with her life just the way it is, thank you. And now if you'll excuse me . . ."

With a smoldering glance directed at her husband, Kim slipped her arm through Dan's as he turned away. "Why don't you come out to the kitchen with me," she said artfully. "I need help refilling the hors d'oeuvres trays, and you look as though you could use a few minutes to cool off."

"You and John—" he began tensely.

"Before you leap to conclusions, I didn't set you up, Dan," Kim said, interrupting him. "I didn't even realize what John and Susan had up their collective sleeves," she added, pushing through the cafe doors into the kitchen, "until a couple of hours ago."

Taking her hand in both of his, Dan turned her so that she was standing in front of him. Too close for comfort, Kim thought, nervous and at the same time feeling strangely excited.

"I'm glad of that, anyway," he said, and his voice was surprisingly gruff. "I wouldn't want anything to spoil the way I've been thinking about you tonight, Kim."

"How was that?" Her voice was scarcely more than a taut whisper. He still held her hand, and now she seemed to hold her breath waiting for his reply.

"The way no man has a right to think of any other man's wife."

* * *

In the living room, Susan was dabbing at her misty eyes with John's monogrammed handkerchief. "It's no use," she moaned. "Dan hasn't changed the way he feels about me."

"Seeing you here tonight was obviously a shock. Give him time, Susan," John advised in his best physician's manner. Comforting grieving relatives was as much a part of his profession as diagnosing and treating illness, and he was a master at it.

"That's exactly what I intend to do," she answered decisively, stuffing the handkerchief back in his breast pocket. "Lots and lots of time—with me." The tears were ended and her mind made up.

"Good girl," John cheered somewhat uneasily. He knew Susan Stewart well enough to suspect that she wouldn't give up in defeat. "Quite honestly, though, I don't see how you're going to get any time with Dan. He struck me as being absolutely clear that the two of you were through."

Susan smiled. "That may be what he thinks. But I'm going to fix it so that Dan has no choice but to see me quite often. Eventually he'll realize just how good a thing we had together. And when he does, I'll be ready for a reconciliation."

John Dixon stared at her, puzzled. "I don't get it, Susan. How do you expect to pull that off?"

"Simple." She moved closer to him and her voice dropped to a conspiratorial whisper. "First thing in the morning, I'm calling my lawyer."

John's eyes widened in surprise. "You mean to get Emily?"

"Exactly. I intend to sue Dan for custody of the child he kidnapped from me. Not that I'm pining away for her, but it's the only way to get Dan back."

"You mean, if you win—" John began.

"What do you mean, *if* I win," she demanded. "No court would deny a heartsick mother her only child. And once I have custody of Emily, Dan will have to come to me to visit her."

John Dixon shook his head with a mixture of awe and admiration over Susan's scheming. Was it just this woman or were all women so devious? he wondered.

If he were able to see into his own kitchen at that moment, he might have discovered the answer.

Carol sank back into the deep, steaming tub until the lilac-scented bubbles were covering all of her except her face. She closed her eyes, and under the relaxing warmth of the bubble bath, the tensions seemed to flow out of her body, allowing her dreams to soar freely. This evening was going to be the most important night of her life, the night she and Tom would put their faltering marriage back together. She'd planned every detail and had spent the entire day getting ready.

Carol wanted everything to be perfect. In spite of the way she had responded to Jay Stallings's unexpected kiss, she did not take her wedding vows lightly. She'd married Tom for better or worse, and she was determined to put the worst behind them and make their marriage better than it had ever been, even in the heady, unforgettable first weeks they had spent as husband and wife.

The extravagant new dress she had bought was laid out on the bed together with the daring new underwear, little more than a wisp of satin and black lace. Downstairs the table was set with candles and her best silver, and in the kitchen a special dinner was cooking. "It has to work; it just has to," she whispered fiercely to herself.

What she and Tom had was too good, too special, to be destroyed by suspicions, mistrust or even a single mistake. Carol preferred to think of Tom's relationship with Natalie Bannon as a mistake. If she admitted it was a betrayal of their marriage vows, of every intimacy they had shared, then it would be so much harder to forgive, impossible to forget.

A mistake, she repeated to herself, like the one she had made with Jay, just as innocent, just as unexpected and just as inexplicable. Even now Carol didn't know what had come over her in Jay's arms. She wasn't ready to face the need, the hunger, the physical desire that had destroyed all caution, all restraint.

Yet she didn't regret it anymore than she blamed Jay for making it happen. His remedy had been perfect. For the first time, Carol felt like a woman whom men could—and did—desire. Tom didn't have to go to anyone else for what he wanted. He could find it right here, with her, and tonight she planned to show him just that.

Scooping up a heaping handful of suds, she massaged her neck, imagining a perfect evening of romance. Finally, she succumbed to the luxuriant ease of the bath.

When she stepped out into the lush embrace of a thick cotton terry towel, Carol was filled with a burning expectation. "Tonight, tonight, won't be just any night," she sang softly as she toweled herself dry. "Tonight . . ."

The telephone rang interrupting her song. Tossing the towel over the shower bar to dry, she walked into the bedroom to answer it.

"Oh, Tom!" She smiled when she heard his voice. "I was hoping it was you. Promise me that tonight you won't be late."

"Actually, Carol, that's why I'm calling." His voice was like a stranger's, full of apologies. "I don't want you to hold dinner for me."

"No, Tom!" She tried to interrupt but it was no use.

"It's been one of those days," he said. "You

know how it is. I'm sorry to stand you up again but—"

"Not tonight. Please, not tonight," she pleaded.

"Look, Carol, don't make a scene, all right? Do you think it's fun for me, putting in eighteen-hour days?" His voice suddenly sounded strange to her, distant, unwelcome.

"It's Natalie, isn't it?" she demanded, unable to hold back the sobs.

"Damn it Carol! How many times do I have to tell you? Natalie is just a new client. It isn't what you think."

"How do you know what I think? You don't even know who I am. When was the last time you really looked at me, talked to me, spent any time with me?" She began to sob convulsively.

"Look, Carol, there's nothing for you to get hysterical about, nothing at all. Trust me, honey, it's not the way it looks. There's nothing between Natalie and me." The aroma of the gourmet dinner she'd worked so hard to prepare wafted up from the kitchen.

"How can you say that to me? How can you come right out and lie to me? What do you think I—" Carol began to argue. Then suddenly, she checked herself. Her anger, her hurt, her disappointment were too great for any words to relieve.

Tom was still talking, still denying everything when she set the receiver back in the cradle. With that single motion, she not only cut him off, she cut him out of her life. The phone began to ring again almost immediately, but Carol didn't answer it. She stared at it blankly, then turned away. Tears spilled unchecked down her cheeks. She wandered through the home she had made with Tom. Once she had imagined she would live here forever. But those days were gone.

As if in a daze, Carol removed the china and silver from the table she had set so lovingly just hours before. In the kitchen she took the seafood casserole out of the oven and dumped the shrimp and lobster down the disposal, then turned it on, listening to it grind as if it were swallowing her marriage up. In the bedroom she carefully folded the daring new underwear and the expensive dress and put them back in their boxes. In the morning she would return them all to the stores where she'd bought them.

Pulling on jeans and a sweater, Carol went into the bathroom and threw some cold water on her face. A couple of bubbles still floated on the murky bath water, a painful reminder of the dreams that would never come true now. What had she done wrong in her marriage? When had she lost Tom? she wondered, draining the water which was now as cold as her heart.

Carol watched until the last drop seeped out. She didn't want any trace of her foolish hopes to remain behind when she walked out of Tom's life. She'd said everything, done everything she could to save her marriage. She'd fought and argued and wept and pleaded and loved and tried to forgive. But Tom's preference was clear. He had made his choice tonight.

Carol could see only one answer left to her. She was too tired to fight anymore, too tired and too hurt. Now she just wanted it all to end. In her dreams the evening was going to be so perfect. Instead it had turned into a nightmare, driving her away from everything she had loved.

Chapter Five

Something Old, Something New

"Thank God I finally found you. I've been looking everywhere." Jay stopped in front of her breathless and pale.

"Why? Is something wrong?" Carol stared at him as if she were seeing a stranger.

"Something is very wrong," he said. "I've been calling you for days and getting no answer."

"I haven't been home. I guess Tom hasn't been either," she said flatly.

"I don't give a damn about Tom. It's you I care about. You gave me an awful scare."

"I'm sorry," Carol mumbled, turning away. "I've been staying at my mother's."

Jay's pulse quickened at the unexpected news, but he was careful not to show his pleasure. "Is that a . . . a permanent move?"

"Is anything in life permanent?" she asked bleakly. "Why were you calling me?"

"It's about the other day, in the car. I was afraid I'd upset you and—"

"No." Carol cut off his apology. "Actually, you made me feel better. It was nice to know that someone cared enough to kiss me, even if the kiss was only therapy."

"You mean . . ." Jay began, afraid even to hope that his deepest wish had finally come true.

She nodded. "Tom and I have split. I was just in his way. You know how it is; there was Tom and Natalie, and three's a crowd." Her voice broke and she turned away, blinking back the tears. She didn't want to break down and make a scene right here in the middle of a shopping mall.

It was all Jay could could do to keep from sweeping her up in his arms and leaping with joy. Instead he grabbed her hand before she could protest and began running down the sidewalk with her, dodging the other shoppers skillfully. "Come on, baby," he murmured, "let's get out of here and go someplace where we can talk."

Half an hour later, they were sitting on the bank of a tiny pond, hidden by weeping willows. Behind them, the branches of the trees bowed so low that they brushed the ground. In front, a family of ducks swam across the placid water. Although Carol's tears had dried, the salt marks still stained her cheeks, and her eyes were red. At Jay's persistent coaxing, she had opened up and told him about the last lonely evening, sparing no detail however painful.

Surprisingly, it had felt good to share her heartbreak with someone, someone who she believed cared about her. Now she lay on the bank, her head cradled in his lap, and gazed up at him.

"Thank you, Jay," she said simply. "It means so much to have a real friend."

"I told you I would always be at your side if you ever needed me," he said, smoothing her hair, which cascaded across his lap in silken waves.

Carol smiled sadly. "I guess I should have trusted you, and come to you sooner."

"I wish you had," he admitted.

Closing her eyes, she felt the sun's warm rays on her face. It was so quiet, she could hear the water lapping at the pond's edge and a squirrel scurrying through the high grass.

"I have a confession to make, too," Jay said finally.

With the lightest touch of his fingertips, he began to trace Carol's face, delineating each feature as he looked down at her anxiously.

"Mmmm," she moaned, his light touch exerting a strange, mesmerizing eroticism that relaxed her and, at the same time, created a sensual tingling through her body. "I thought you were the father confessor."

"It's about the other day," he said, ignoring her teasing words, "in the car when I kissed you."

For an instant the silence returned. Then she whispered, barely audibly, "I remember."

Bending over her so that his lips almost grazed hers, Jay said, "Carol, that kiss wasn't only therapy."

She opened her eyes and found that her lashes were brushing his cheek. "I don't understand," she whispered.

"I think you do, but maybe this will make it clearer."

She didn't move as his lips descended and closed over hers in the gentlest, most tender kiss she had ever received. And she didn't move as his mouth left hers and began a slow, compelling tour of her face. By the time he had visited her cheeks, her forehead, the bridge of her nose, her fluttering eyelids, and was covering her throat with light, hungry kisses, Carol's breath was coming in short, quick gasps. Still, she didn't try to stop him.

"You're so beautiful, Carol," Jay said in an awed whisper. "I've dreamed of being with you like this so many days, so many nights." His voice was like a lullaby, calming her, but his strong hands were like a storm, catching her body up in its torrent. Sinking back into the grass, she surrendered to the waves of emotion that washed over her.

"I want to make love to you, Carol," Jay murmured, his voice tense with the desire he had held back for so long, "but only if you want me to."

Carol didn't know what she wanted. She'd been hurt so deeply by Tom's betrayal, nothing seemed to matter anymore. But Jay wanted her. In some secret part of her mind, she'd known that for a long time, even before his kiss. But she'd never allowed herself to think about it until now. Jay was kind to her in a way Tom never had been. She remembered the way she had answered his kiss. Did she want him, too? She didn't know. She wasn't sure of anything except the pain that she'd been living with ever since she began to suspect Tom of having an affair with Natalie. And now for the first time that pain was easing. Jay's hands and lips, his kisses and caresses, were making her forget.

"Yes," she murmured. "Yes."

He gazed at her, wanting her desperately yet afraid to add to her hurt. "Are you sure, Carol? You've got to be sure."

She nodded mutely. Her eyes were luminous with tears. All she wanted to do was forget, forget Tom, the husband she had loved so totally, forget their marriage which had begun so happily.

"I love you more than I can ever tell you. I'll never hurt you," Jay whispered, taking her in his arms. "I want to marry you, Carol, and take care of you forever," he murmured against the lobe of her ear. "Will you let me, baby?" he pleaded, plucking a dandelion that had caught in her hair.

In her heart, Carol believed that she would never love again. How could she give herself to any man the way she had surrendered to Tom? How could she ever trust anyone so blindly again? It wouldn't be fair to Jay if she said yes. And yet she needed someone to hold her, someone to ease the anguish in her heart, and Jay was so willing. She tried to tell herself she liked him only as a friend, but how could she when her body was responding so totally to his touch?

It had been so long since she and Tom had made love freely—without the thought of Natalie coming between them—that Jay's tender touch, the strength of his desire, the power of his love was kindling a blaze of passion deep within her. She felt herself being swept up in a tidal wave of desire that was erasing every fear, every reservation. Her mind locked shut and her body carried her into his arms. No memories could intrude, no inhibitions, no second thoughts. They were no longer Carol Hughes and Jay Stallings but just a woman in need and a man very much in love.

"Yes! Yes, Jay!" Carol cried out.

He answered her with a kiss that sealed their future in the ecstasy of a single moment.

Tom lay back in Natalie's big canopied bed, his hand stroking back a loose tendril of hair. He sighed deeply. "We make some pair, don't we?"

"Mmmm," she murmured, stretching and flopping over onto her belly.

Turning onto his side, Tom ran his hand along the length of her back, beginning at her neck and gliding down along the warm, silken highway of her spine. "What would you say if I asked you to marry me?"

Natalie laughed. "I'd say," she answered, "to run home to the little woman and stop wasting my time with dumb questions."

"I'm serious, Natalie." Tom took her by the shoulders and gazed into her face, a classic and classy face, the bones strong, the features fine and even, the eyes luminous. "Will you marry me?"

For a moment, she stared back at him incredulously, then she turned away. The desire that had been so strong seconds before dissipated suddenly. She hadn't expected this from Tom and didn't welcome it. "You mean your wife has finally left you?" she said coldly.

Tom's eyes flashed angrily. "Is that all you can say, Natalie? For God's sake, I just asked you to marry me."

"What happened?" she asked sarcastically, ignoring his anger. "Did the whiz kid finally figure out what you and I have been working at night after night? I suppose she packed her bags and ran home to Mama."

"Cut it out, Natalie," he commanded. "I told you to leave Carol out of it."

"Why? Is she too good for me to ever mention her name?"

"She's a great girl, that's all, and I feel lousy about what I've done to her, the way I've treated her. She doesn't deserve it," Tom admitted.

"Sure, I know how it is," Natalie countered. "You feel lousy. But not lousy enough to kiss *me* good-bye."

"Come off it," Tom grumbled, unwilling to admit how right her charge was. "I just don't want to talk about Carol now. I want to talk about us."

Natalie rolled away and lay on her back, staring up at the ceiling. She'd never expected Tom's wife to walk out on him—at least not without any warning. Natalie didn't like to be caught off guard. She liked to have her answers ready.

Marry Tom Hughes? It wasn't a question she'd even considered seriously. Tom was safely married to a woman he seemed to genuinely care for. That's why she'd felt free to go as far as she liked with him. There were no strings, no attachments. It was an affair that made no real demands on Natalie. There was only one man in the world Natalie had ever thought seriously of settling down with —Luke Porter. She shut her eyes remembering. Luke was the reason she'd left Kilborn and moved to Oakdale. Did he even care? Did he ever miss her? Luke!

"Damn it, Natalie. I didn't expect you to fall asleep when I asked you to be my wife," Tom snapped, interrupting her thoughts. "At least not before you answered."

"I'm not asleep," she said without opening her eyes.

"Then what are you doing?"

"Thinking."

"About your answer?"

"Something like that."

"I thought," he began, surprised and hurt that she hadn't rushed to say yes, "after we made such terrific love—"

"Is that what you call it?" she interrupted, more harshly than she'd intended. "I thought we just had sex."

"You mean you don't want to marry me. That's what you're telling me, isn't it?" He sank back in the pillow, feeling confused and defeated.

It had never occurred to Tom when he started seeing Natalie that Carol would ever leave him. He had been sure that she loved him too much to walk out on him, even if he deserved it. He felt lousy about the way he'd treated her. But even more than that, he felt hurt. Carol hadn't wasted any time suing for divorce or snagging a rich new husband. That was the hottest bit of gossip in Oakdale, anyway: Carol Hughes and Jay Stallings.

Tom didn't want to believe it. He didn't want to think of Carol with another man. But when he called her, hoping to hear her say it wasn't true, she had refused to speak to him. Her mother had assured him it was true, though. Carol had accepted Jay's proposal. All the time with Natalie, Tom had worried that he'd been hurting Carol. Instead, it looked as if she couldn't have cared less. He didn't believe it, couldn't accept it, even if it was true. But damn it, if she didn't care about what they had together, then neither would he. He didn't want to be alone, and he and Natalie were damned good to-gether.

"I didn't say that I didn't want to marry you, Tom," Natalie finally said, a certain, uncharacteristic hesitation in her voice.

"Well, you're not exactly rushing to say I do," he pointed out.

"Should I be?"

"What do you mean?"

"I mean, do you really want to marry me or are you just trying to show Carol that you don't need her?"

Angry that his thoughts were so transpar-ent, Tom grabbed Natalie roughly by the shoulders and pinned her against the mattress. "What did I tell you?" he demanded threateningly. "Leave my wife out of this!"

Natalie opened her eyes and stared up at him, excited by the barely suppressed violence in his tone. Her dark eyes smoldered with fire. "Well, what are you waiting for?" she breathed huskily.

"An answer."

"Don't you hear me, Tom?" she whispered, reaching up to kiss him.

"Stop playing games and answer me, damn it," he swore.

"Yes. Yes," she whispered, "if you promise you'll make love to me all night every night. That's the only marriage vow I want you to make."

"I, Tom Hughes, solemnly swear," he promised, showering her face with kisses.

Natalie closed her eyes and surrendered to the feelings that propelled them. Together, they reached new heights of passion. Swept away by the moment, Natalie cried out for the one man she'd never forget.

Tom was too caught up in the fury of their lovemaking to heed her words. In his fevered mind, he thought she was saying, "Love." Instead, Natalie was moaning, "Luke! Luke!"

Lying back when their passion had subsided, Natalie looked at the man she'd just promised to marry. It was true, they did make a great pair, she admitted to herself. But the thought brought her little comfort. She couldn't marry Tom; she didn't love him. There was only one man in the world she had ever wanted to marry, and he wasn't lying beside her.

Chapter Six
Thorns Among the Roses

A bouquet of June roses clutched behind his back, Grant Coleman paced the length of the hospital solarium and back. He had covered those same steps more times than he cared to remember. When Joyce had been rushed to the emergency room with a ruptured appendix, he had paced waiting to hear if the surgery had been successful. Now two weeks later Grant was pacing for a very different reason. Joyce was out of the woods. In fact, she was scheduled to be released the following day, and Lisa was pressing him to insist on a divorce now, while Joyce was still vulnerable. He'd seen her through her operation and recovery. Now, according to Lisa's shrewd calculations, Joyce was in his debt.

Grant had come to the hospital to do what

he felt he must, but wished there were some other way. There was nothing he hated more than creating a scene, but unfortunately his wife thrived on them. Steeling himself for the encounter ahead, Grant walked slowly down the corridor to Joyce's room and knocked on the door. Her voice sounded strong and bright when she called, "Come in."

"Oh Grant," she gushed when she saw him, "you brought me pink roses! You still remember they're my favorite. Why it's just like old times. The first year we were married you brought me a pink rose every day. Three hundred sixty-five pink rosebuds because you said they matched my complexion perfectly. You were so romantic." She beamed up at him from the bed. It was raised so that she was sitting back against a brace of pillows. Her dark hair was freshly brushed and formed a soft frame around her face, which was, indeed, flushed as pink as the roses.

Grant had no choice but to give her the flowers, even though he now wished he hadn't brought them. "Actually, Joyce," he said coldly, "they're supposed to be a peace offering."

"They're much more than that to me, Grant," she cooed, "especially now when things aren't as wonderful as they might be between us."

"That's the understatement of the year," he retorted. "In fact, it's what I came by to talk to you about."

"I thought you wanted to see how I was feeling." She fingered the velvet-soft petal of a rosebud. "I am still recovering from major surgery, you know."

Grant sighed in exasperation. Why was it that he could never spend five minutes with Joyce without becoming thoroughly irritated? "Let's not play games with each other," he pleaded. "Just for once, let's try to have an honest, open discussion about our futures, instead of keeping up the ridiculous charade that we're still husband and wife in anything except name."

"I can only speak for myself, of course, Grant," she said with saccharine sweetness. "But as far as I'm concerned, you're just as much my husband now as you were on our wedding day. I'll never let anything change that."

"That was changed a long time ago, Joyce," Grant said, trying not to let his temper get the better of him. "So why don't you stop playing games. I want a divorce. It's as simple as that. Now let's sit down together like two mature adults and talk about it."

Joyce's eyes filled with tears. Grant hated to see her cry. He'd do just about anything, she knew, to avoid it. "I want to talk, Grant, because I want to be a good wife to you if you'll only give me a second chance." She reached for a tissue from the bedside table and dabbed at her eyes. "Give our marriage a second chance. We had so much going for us, and we can again."

"Joyce, will you please listen to me for once," he pleaded. "Our marriage is over. Maybe we're both to blame, I don't know. And at this point, I don't really care. Our marriage was a mistake from the beginning."

"How can you say that?" she cried. "Don't you remember the Christmas you gave me the sapphire earrings, or the trip to Mexico when we found that beautiful little beach, or—"

"Please, Joyce!" Grant found himself shouting. "What are you raking up all that for? You sound like a human scrapbook."

"You do remember, don't you?" she insisted, her eyes glistening with tears.

"Of course I remember. But all that's over. You're talking about the past, Joyce. And I want to talk about the present—and the future."

"Oh, so do I!" she said, stifling a sob. "Our future, Grant. I just know it can be as marvelous as those early days were, if you'll only give me a chance to show you."

He tried to interrupt, but she wouldn't let him. "No, let me finish, please," Joyce insisted. "I know you were unhappy with me. But I've been so lonely since you left that I've had a lot of time to think about us, and what I can do differently. I know you want a divorce, and I'll give it to you, but first I want to try again. Come back home, please, Grant. If it doesn't work out this time, then you can do whatever you want. But first I want a reconciliation." Although Joyce's voice had risen to a petulant whine, her stubbornness was clear in the firm set of her mouth as she waited for his answer.

Grant stared at his wife as if he couldn't believe what he was hearing. "A reconciliation?" he echoed. "Is this your idea of a joke, Joyce? Because if it is, it's a very bad one."

"I've never been more serious in my life, Grant. You're my husband, and I'm not going to throw away our marriage license as if it were yesterday's paper."

"But there is absolutely nothing to reconcile," he pointed out sharply. "We haven't spent a day without wanting to kill each other in I can't remember how many years."

"That's the trouble with you," she sniffled. "You just think about the problems we've had. But . . ."

"Damn it, Joyce, there are no buts," he exclaimed. "A reconciliation is out of the question. I'm going to remarry, or have you conveniently forgotten that little detail?"

Joyce reached for another tissue and realized the time for halfway measures was over. She'd managed to stall Grant again and again, but where had it gotten her? If anything, he was more persistent than he'd ever been. Joyce was sure the divorce was not his idea. It was that conniving Lisa Shea, the most notorious husband hunter in town. When it came to women Grant was a fool.

Didn't he know how many husbands Lisa had run through already? What made him think that he'd be any different?

Joyce knew that her husband would become defensive if she tried to point out the truth about Lisa to him. Much as she'd love to lash out at the woman he wanted to marry, Joyce was too shrewd to express her bitterness. She wasn't going to let Grant accuse her of jealousy, even though she was green with it. Somehow she had to make him feel that he wasn't playing fair, that he was taking advantage of her.

Wadding the tissue into a ball, she pretended to stem the flood of tears that were falling freely now. With a little cry of pain, she sank back into the pillows and closed her eyes tightly. Her face contorted in what she hoped looked like an anguished grimace.

"Are you all right, Joyce?" he asked hesitantly.

She heard the concern in his voice with secret glee. "I'll be fine, just fine—" Her voice caught with a gasp and she clutched her stomach where the incision had been made. "—in a minute."

"You look like you're in pain."

"It's nothing," she murmured weakly. "It will pass. All things pass, even love, husbands, marriage. That's what you believe, isn't it?"

"That's not the important thing now," he

said brusquely. "If you're in pain, Joyce, I should get a doctor."

"No, no more doctors." She put her hand across her forehead. "If they see me like this, they won't let me go home tomorrow."

"Maybe you shouldn't. There's no need to rush things."

"But there is, don't you see, there is, Grant," she said, gasping. "You're forcing me to with all this pressure for an instant divorce. I have to get out of here. There are lawyers to talk to and papers to find, a whole life to end."

He felt more guilty with every word. Though Grant hated to admit it, this time, Joyce was right. He was pushing her too hard and too fast for his own selfish reasons. What happiness would he and Lisa enjoy if it were gained at the expense of Joyce's health?

"I'm sorry," he apologized contritely. "I had no idea you were still in such pain. I never would have talked to you so harshly if I did. The most important thing now is for you to get well again. That's what both Lisa and I want. We don't want to hurt you, Joyce. We just want to be free to make our own life. Can you understand that?"

Joyce forced a weak smile. "Of course I'll try to, Grant," she lied. "You know I would do anything in the world for you. But if you don't mind, I'm still so weak from the operation. I don't know what's the matter with me.

Dr. Dixon says it just takes time to recover from surgery as serious as mine."

"You've talked to him about the way you feel then?" he asked. How could Dixon allow a patient to be discharged who hadn't fully recovered? he wondered. With so many malpractice cases crowding the courts, it would be suicidal for any doctor. And Dixon, whatever his personal shortcomings, was a responsible physician.

Joyce nodded. "We had a long talk yesterday—actually an argument, I guess you'd call it. I told him how urgent it was for me to be discharged as soon as possible. Of course he said I was in no condition to go home for another week to ten days and even then I should take it very easy. But I kept thinking of you, Grant. I knew you'd begin pressing me for a divorce again just because I'm out of intensive care. You're so impetuous. Finally we compromised. I can go home as long as I have someone come in to take care of me. And," she added, sneaking a glance at him to see if he was swallowing her story, "I'm not supposed to be upset for any reason."

Grant's dark eyes were fixed on her intensely and his gaunt face was drawn in a frown. "Maybe I should have a talk with Dixon, Joyce. I had no idea—"

"No," she interrupted with a panic-stricken cry. "That won't be necessary,

Grant," she added calming herself. "Remember, I have to learn how to get along by myself now. That's what you want, isn't it?"

"Yes, but . . ."

"No buts. You said so yourself," she insisted.

"Okay, if that's the way you want it," he agreed with a certain reluctance. "Is there anything I *can* do for you, Joyce?"

"Yes, there is one thing," she began, fidgeting with the edge of the sheet as if she didn't really want to ask the favor. "I still feel so weak, I don't think I could bear the pressure of a divorce right now. If you could give me a little more time . . . just until I get back on my feet."

Grant turned away in silence. Joyce looked small and pathetic in the hospital bed, her face red from crying, her eyes pleading for a single favor. Although he suspected that she was just stalling for more time, he was moved. She *had* undergone major surgery and maybe, just maybe, she really did need more time to convalesce.

"Okay, Joyce," he agreed with a deep sigh. "You win this round." But even as he capitulated, Grant was wondering how he was going to tell Lisa that they would have to wait a little longer.

"Carol Hughes, bride of Mr. Jay Stallings." Lisa read the newspaper headline aloud. The story of the wedding was accompanied by a two-column photograph of the bride. Carol was wearing a broad-brimmed organdy hat and smiling as if she had found perfect happiness at last. "The bride wore a pale yellow organdy ankle-length dress with a square neck and cap sleeves. A matching hat framed her face. She carried a bouquet of miniature yellow daylilies." Lisa read half aloud and half to herself.

Putting down the Sunday paper, she glanced across the breakfast table at her son, a bittersweet smile playing at the corners of her mouth. "Carol still makes a beautiful bride," she said with a sigh.

"She certainly does," Tom admitted, trying not to let his mother see how much he still cared.

"A June bride. That's what I was going to be. Now it looks like August at the earliest if we're lucky. Grant is hopeful. . . ." She touched the corners of her eyes with her napkin. Weddings always made her cry, especially when they didn't come off. "But that's another story. I want to hear about you, Tom," she went on, blinking back the tears and refocusing her attention on her son. "I still can't understand how you let Carol get away from you. She was the perfect wife."

"Sometimes perfection can be tough to live with every day." Tom frowned with irritation. He knew he wasn't being fair to Carol, but he didn't want to discuss her with his mother, especially today when she was probably just waking up from her wedding night. "Jay Stallings is a lucky guy, so am I ever since Natalie agreed to marry me."

"I hope you're as lucky as you think," Lisa said coolly.

"Come on, give the girl a chance," Tom begged. "You're going to like Natalie when you meet her. I know the two of you will get along great. Actually, she's a lot like you. She's tough and beautiful and always gets what she wants."

"Thanks. You certainly know how to give a compliment," Lisa retorted. "But I still believe Carol was the best woman for you, and I don't think I'd change my mind if you brought a madonna around here."

"Okay. You've made your point," he said hotly. "Now, if you don't mind, I'd like you to drop it. I'll admit it if it will make you feel better. Maybe I did make a mistake letting Carol go, but see that?" He pointed angrily at the paper lying on the table in front of her. "That's how much she loved me. That's how much she cared. Jay Stallings! It makes me sick to think of them."

"How do you think it must have made her feel to think of you and Natalie?" Lisa reminded him.

Tom shook his head, refusing to admit the truth in his mother's words. "That was different. Anyway, I said I made a mistake. What more do you want from me? After all, your record in the marriage department hasn't exactly been a model."

"I'm the first to admit that I've made mistakes—lots of them," Lisa agreed, pouring coffee for them both. "That's why I'm so concerned about you."

"Well, don't be," he assured her with a ready smile. "Natalie and I are going to be very happy together. We understand each other."

"I don't know," Lisa persisted. "From what I've heard about her, she sounds like another Meredith Halliday."

"You really hated Meredith, didn't you?" Tom accused.

"No, I didn't hate the girl," she protested. "I just knew she was very wrong for you. She would have brought you nothing but trouble. And now this Natalie . . ."

"At least give her a chance," Tom broke in angrily. "You haven't even met Natalie yet, and you're already against her. Carol isn't the only decent woman in the world, you know."

Lisa sighed and sipped her coffee, trying not to let her eyes wander back to the wedding picture. "You're right, Tom, and I'm sorry. I'm not being fair to either you or your new girlfriend. I was so fond of Carol that it's hard for me to accept the fact that it really is over between you two. You may not think I'm the grandmotherly type, but I'd been sort of hoping you and Carol would have a child. I'd like for once to have a real family."

"Maybe Natalie and I will have kids," he said, reaching over to squeeze her hand. "Or you and Grant," he teased.

She laughed harshly. "Grant and I? I'm beginning to think that we'll be collecting Social Security before we get married."

"You mean Grant's divorce still isn't final?" Tom asked incredulously. It seemed as if his own marriage to Carol had been dissolved before he even had time to understand what he was losing.

"Not final!" Lisa echoed bitterly. "It isn't even in the works yet. That awful wife of his is still trying to get him back. She's tried every game you've ever heard of and then some. You wouldn't believe some of the things she's pulled, Tom. But it's not going to work. Grant is going to be mine sooner or later."

"Gosh, I had no idea," Tom admitted. "I just figured you were taking your own sweet time about getting hooked again."

"Not at all. If I had my way, we would have been married weeks ago. But I'm being very patient and understanding for Grant's sake . . . and to show up Joyce Coleman for what she is." Lisa smiled maliciously. "She's behaving so terribly that the contrast is inescapable."

"It's hard to picture you in the role of the sweet little woman waiting at home with her knitting," Tom teased.

"Not nearly as hard as it is to play the part convincingly," she countered with a deep laugh.

"Poor Joyce Coleman," he said and grinned. "If she only knew whom she was up against, she'd throw in the towel."

"I wish it were that simple, Tom. But you still have a lot to learn about women," his mother reminded him.

"I have a feeling that Natalie is going to be almost as good a teacher as you," he said with a mischievous gleam in his eye.

"Do you really love her, Tom?" Lisa asked, dropping the bantering tone and becoming very serious. "Because if you don't, your marriage won't last. Take it from me, Tom. I know from unfortunate experience what I'm talking about."

"Don't worry. Natalie and I are fantastic together," he assured her, trying to recapture the joking tone of their conversation.

"I'm sure you are, but are you in love?"

"I'm never bored with her, and I can't imagine ever getting tired of her. That's not bad for openers."

"It could be worse," she admitted grudgingly. "I just hope you're not going to rush into this new marriage."

"You mean on the rebound?"

"Something like that." Lisa reached over and took his hand in hers. "I know I haven't been much of a mother to you, so I don't really have a right to tell you what you should and shouldn't do with your life. But I love you, Tom, and I want you to be happy."

"I am happy," he insisted.

She shook her head, unconvinced. "I just hope you know what you're doing, because when you've made as many mistakes in your life as I have, it's difficult to sit by and watch your son follow in your footsteps."

"Marrying Natalie isn't a mistake," he insisted. "It's what I want and what she wants. How can I make you believe that?"

Shrugging her shoulders, Lisa forced herself to smile. "Just let me ask you one other thing about Natalie and then I'll get off your back, I promise."

"Okay. Shoot."

"What do you know about the girl?"

"What do you mean?"

"Exactly what I said. Where is she from? Do you know her friends? Have you met her family? What does she do? You know, the basic facts of her life."

"She's from Kilborn, and I don't really give a damn which side of the tracks she's from. My family history wouldn't exactly inspire confidence in a bride to be."

"That was a cheap shot," Lisa said sharply.

"I'm sorry. I only meant to say that I know all I want to about Natalie, and I'm not interested in any inquisitions," Tom replied firmly. But if he had known what Natalie was doing at that very moment, he wouldn't have answered with such confidence.

Chapter Seven
Winners Take All

"Grant!" Lisa cried, leaping to her feet in his office as if she were prepared to wage a battle royal. "You make it sound as though she had a heart transplant. Her appendix ruptured! It's out, and that's it. I was married to a doctor once, remember? I should know that much anyway."

She looked crisp and cool, dressed in a peach linen double-breasted suit with navy and white pumps and a matching handbag, but inwardly Lisa was seething. No wonder he didn't want to discuss his visit with Joyce over the phone, she thought angrily.

Grant shrugged helplessly. He hadn't been able to pressure Joyce, and now he couldn't calm Lisa. "She was so convincing, darling," he insisted awkwardly.

"Is she really that good an actress? Or were you just willing to be convinced?"

"What do you mean by that?" he demanded, feeling trapped between the two possessive women.

Inhaling deeply, Lisa counted to ten under her breath. It wouldn't do any good to let Grant see what she really thought about the way his wife had manipulated him. Fluffing her hair nervously with one hand, she sat on the corner of his desk. It was a broad mahogany desk with a leather top, polished to a high gloss. The legal briefs and correspondence were stacked neatly. There were no photographs, no personal mementos at all except a silver letter opener shaped like a dagger.

"Nothing," she said contritely. "I'm sorry, darling. I'm green with jealousy and I can't help myself."

"You've been very patient, Lisa, and understanding. I can't ask for anything more," he said, leaning forward so that he could touch her arm reassuringly.

"I'm afraid my patience is running thin," she confessed.

He gave her a quick smile. "Mine, too."

Picking up the letter opener, Lisa toyed with it nervously. "Tell me something, Grant," she said finally. "Do you still love Joyce?"

"No." His answer was quick and firm. Still she wasn't totally satisfied.

"You do feel protective though, don't you?"

"I guess maybe I do in a way." Grant answered slowly as if he were considering her question carefully. "Old habits are hard to break, and she was always so dependent." For a long moment neither of them spoke. Although she knew Grant was watching her, Lisa didn't look at him. Finally he said so softly that she wasn't sure if he had spoken or if it was her imagination, "How about you?"

"What do you mean?" she faltered.

Grant's eyes were boring deep into her soul, demanding the whole truth. "Michael Shea," he said flatly.

"He's dead."

"Yes, but in your heart?"

Glancing at him, she gave a short, bitter laugh. "He's been dead in my heart even longer. I've never told you much about him because I haven't wanted to remember. It was not a happy marriage. In fact it wasn't even a willing one."

"What do you mean?"

Lisa closed her eyes for a moment and remembered her former husband as she'd first seen him. "Dr. Michael Shea," she began, a hint of tension coloring her voice, "was gorgeous and charming, but both qualities were only skin deep. Scratch that attractive veneer, and you'd find a superheel. He was only out for himself. Michael could have been a fine doctor, if he weren't so power hungry and greedy. Somehow I never saw any of his faults until it was too late. At the time I was so infatuated that I had a child by him . . . my youngest son, Chuck. Of course, Michael had a wife—that kind always does—a very wealthy, socially prominent wife who could give him the status and the life-style he craved. That's why he wouldn't divorce her, even to give our son a name.

"Much later, after I'd finally woken up to what he really was, he wanted to marry me. His wife had found out about our affair by then and had divorced him, and Michael had suddenly discovered the joys of fatherhood. I think Chuck was the only person Michael ever truly loved."

"You don't have to tell me any of this, Lisa," Grant interrupted gently.

"But I want to," she insisted. "It's not a very pretty story, and it's not a part of my life I like to remember. But I'd rather you hear it from me now than from someone else. And believe me, one day some malicious gossip in Oakdale is bound to tell you about my scandalous past."

"You mean forewarned is forearmed?" he said thoughtfully.

Lisa smiled a little wistfully. "Something like that, I guess."

"You did marry Michael Shea, though," Grant reminded her like the skillful lawyer he was, "after you realized the true character of the man."

"Yes, counselor," she admitted wryly, "I

did but not freely. He blackmailed me into marriage."

"Blackmail?" Grant echoed incredulously.

For a moment Lisa covered her face with her hands as if protecting herself from the bitter memories. Then she said, "My son, Tom, came back from Vietnam hooked on drugs. There wasn't anything bad about him, he was just a mixed-up kid who couldn't deal with what he'd seen and done. Michael caught him stealing drugs in the hospital and threatened me. Either I agreed to marry him or he'd turn Tom in."

"Some choice," Grant murmured sympathetically.

Turning away, Lisa walked to the window and gazed out, clasping and unclasping her hands nervously. The street below was crowded with workers rushing to grab a quick lunch or cram an hour of shopping into their busy day. By contrast, Grant's office seemed almost unnaturally quiet, as if it was somehow removed from the rest of the world.

"I did what I think any mother would do. I married Michael Shea," she said finally. Smiling to herself, she went on. "Poor Michael. He was so sure he'd won just because he'd gotten me to stand up in front of a judge and say 'I do.' But I wasn't going to let any man force his way into my bed. Our marriage was a farce. I made a point of teasing Michael by wearing the sexiest nightgowns I could find, then locking him out of my room. Finally, he got so mad, he said he was going to court to take Chuck away from me because I was an unfit mother. That was one threat too many," Lisa said, tensing even now at the memory. "I was so scared, I took my son and flew to Mexico. You know the rest of the sordid story—everyone in town does—about Michael's murder and Tom's trial."

"It's good somebody killed him," Grant muttered under his breath, "and spared me the pleasure."

For another long, silent moment, Lisa stared blindly down on the street scene below, too wrapped up in her own thoughts to see or hear anything.

"So now you know all about Lisa Shea's scandalous past," she said, turning back to face him at last. To her surprise, Grant was standing in front of her. She hadn't heard him leave his desk and cross the office. Looking up at him, she finished softly, "I won't blame you a bit, if you go back to Joyce now."

"I'm not going anywhere, Lisa," he promised, taking her into his arms and holding her close. "At least not without you. Don't you understand? I don't care about your past. You're a woman who has lived and suffered and learned. That's what's important to me —that and our future."

"Are you sure, Grant?" she asked, afraid to believe in what he was saying.

Soaps & Serials™ Fans!

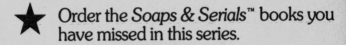

★ Order the *Soaps & Serials*™ books you have missed in this series.

★ Collect other *Soaps & Serials*™ series from their very beginnings.

★ Give *Soaps & Serials*™ series as gifts to other fans.

...see other side for ordering information

Soaps & Serials™
From Pioneer Communications
Network, Inc.

You can now order previous titles of *Soaps & Serials*™ Books by mail!

Just complete the order form, detach, and send together with your check or money order payable to:

Soaps & Serials™
120 Brighton Road, Box 5201
Clifton, NJ 07015-5201

Please <u>circle</u> the book #'s you wish to order:

The Young and The Restless	1	2	3	4	5	6	7
Days of Our Lives......	1	2	3	4	5	6	7
Guiding Light	1	2	3	4	5	6	7
Another World.........	1	2	3	4	5	6	7
As The World Turns....	1	2	3	4	5	6	7
Dallas™	1	2	3	4	5	6	7
Knots Landing™	1	2	3	4	5	6	7
Capitol™................	1	2	3	4	NOT AVAILABLE		

Each book is $2.50 ($3.50 in Canada).

Total number of books
circled _____ × price above = $ _____ .

Sales tax (CT and NY residents only) $ _____ .

Shipping and Handling $ _____ .95

Total payment enclosed $ _____ .
(check or money orders only)

Name _____

Address _____ Apt# _____

City _____

State _____ Zip _____

Telephone (_____) _____
　　　　Area code

ATWT 7

"Will this convince you?" he murmured, crushing her lips with his. For a magical moment as they met in a kiss that drove every anguished memory from her mind, Lisa knew only that she had found the man she had searched for so long.

"There is one other thing that means a lot to me right now," Grant said, breaking away from her seductive lips while he still could.

"What's that?" she asked fearfully. She wished their kiss could have gone on forever so they wouldn't have to speak. Words were so dangerous, so full of ambiguities, so easily misunderstood.

"Lunch!" Grant grinned broadly. "I thought we had a date."

Linking her arm through his, Lisa laughed. "I'm starved."

"Me too," he said, burning her with the gaze of his deep, dark eyes. "But I don't think there's anything on the menu of the Townesend Oyster House that will satisfy my appetite today. In fact," he added with a wicked grin, "I don't think anything can, until I take you in my arms as my wife."

Glancing over his shoulder nervously, Dan Stewart saw that the courtroom was empty except for a few curious spectators and one bored court reporter, chewing on a toothpick in the pressbox. Across the aisle, Susan sat between two lawyers. The wronged mother, he thought angrily. She was dressed perfectly for the part in a demure navy blue dress that looked modest without being severe, and she made a point of turning often to smile at the little girl who was perched on his lap, looking all around with wide, innocent eyes.

Instinctively, Dan's arms tightened around his daughter's tiny waist as the court officer intoned sternly, "Will Miss Emily Stewart please take the stand?" He turned to his attorney, hoping for an objection, but the lawyer shook his head.

"She's got to testify," he whispered. "I never thought she'd be called as a witness or I would have warned you."

"Thanks for nothing," Dan muttered under his breath.

"What did you say, Daddy?" Emily turned to him with wide, questioning eyes.

"See that man up there, honey, sitting behind the big desk?" Dan pointed to the judge. "He wants to talk to you. So you run up and sit in that big chair beside him. I'll be right here the whole time, so you don't have to be frightened."

"You mean the man in the black dress?" Emily piped up loud enough to produce a titter of adult laughter. "He looks funny."

We'll see just how funny he is, Dan thought bleakly as he watched Emily trot up and take the witness chair. Her head was just visible over the top of the stand. Then she knelt up and waved excitedly. "Hi, Daddy!"

Dan waved back and blew her a kiss,

feeling a great lump of love and fear constrict his throat. Why was Susan putting them through this painful public procedure? She didn't want Emily. She'd never wanted Emily or any other child.

"Is that your father over there?" The judge was leaning down from his bench and speaking kindly to the little girl. Inexplicably, Dan thought of the wolf in grandmother's clothing. He'd read the story of Red Riding Hood to the girls the night before, and Emily had laughed, too little to imagine that a wicked wolf might lurk in her own life.

Now she was nodding vigorously to the judge's question and waving again.

"Do you love your daddy?"

"Of course I love my daddy, silly," she answered as if it was the most ridiculous question she'd ever heard.

"And how about that lady over there?" the judge asked, pointing to Susan. "Do you know who she is?"

He frowned as Emily shook her head. "Do you love your mother, Emily?"

She looked up at the judge and said clearly, "I don't have a mommy."

"Everyone has a mother, Emily," he corrected. "Does your father ever talk to you about your mother?"

She shook her head. "Betsy doesn't have a mommy either," she volunteered. "Her mommy died, but she loved Betsy very much. Daddy said so."

"I think your mother loves you, too," the judge told her.

"But I don't have a mommy. I told you," Emily repeated patiently.

The judge leaned closer and smiled down at her. "Would you like to have a mother?"

"Oh, yes," Emily exclaimed. "If she's pretty."

"That lady sitting over there is very pretty, don't you think?"

Susan smiled as if on cue, and Emily nodded uncertainly. "I guess."

"Well, Emily," the judge began in a voice that he was sure sounded wise and reasonable. "That lady sitting right there is your mother, and she loves you so much that she would like you to go and live with her."

For a moment, Emily's fair eyebrows knitted in a picture of puzzlement, then she suddenly smiled again. "No, thank you very much," she said, remembering that she was supposed to speak politely to adults. "I live with my daddy." And then, before the officer could stop her, she darted down from the witness box and ran across the court into her father's outstretched arms.

Dan caught her and hugged her, too overcome to speak or do anything except bury his face in her downy hair. But the judge was unmoved. Gaveling the proceedings into order again, he began to gather his papers together. "The court finds in favor of the natural mother, Susan Stewart, and grants her full custody of her daughter, Emily," he said without looking directly at either plaintiff or defendant. "Effective immediately. The father, Daniel Stewart, is granted unrestricted visiting rights."

Dan lived through the next moments as if they were a dream. The court was adjourned, the judge stepped down and disappeared into his chambers, Chris Hughes, his attorney, commiserated. But Dan didn't care. The only thing with any reality for him at that moment was the feel of Emily's arms wrapped tightly around his neck and the softness of her cheek pressed securely against his.

Although he knew what the judge had said, he couldn't believe it would actually happen until Susan crossed the aisle.

"Come on, Emily," she said, her voice soft and coaxing. "It's time to come home." Reaching out, she tried to stroke the child's hair, but Emily shrank from her touch.

Susan looked from the child to her father with what she hoped was an expression of understanding and concern. "I'm sorry, Dan. I wish—for all our sakes—there could be some other way. But Emily is my daughter, too."

"There is such a thing as joint custody," he glared at her furiously. "You could have asked for that, Susan."

"I could have . . . if I could trust you to abide by it," she answered calmly. "But given your past record . . ."

Emily's eyes had grown huge and frightened as they spoke, and now she looked from her mother to her father. Although she hadn't understood their words, somehow she had managed to sense their meaning.

"I love you, Daddy," she said, hugging him even tighter.

"And I love you, too, baby," he assured her although he was barely able to say the simple words. "I always will. You'll never know how much."

He held her so fiercely that she complained. "Ouch, you're hurting me, Daddy."

"Mommy loves you, too, Emily." Susan leaned over and held out her hand to the child. "Why don't you come for a walk with me and I'll tell you all about it. Then I'll tell you all about the wonderful things we're going to do together. Maybe we'll go to a toy store and you can pick out anything you want."

"A baby doll?" Emily looked up brightly.

"If that's what you want," Susan promised, "with a bottle and a cradle, just like a real baby's."

For a moment, Emily seemed on the verge of going with Susan. The offer was tempting. But some deep instinct made her hold back. "Can Daddy come too?" she asked.

"Your daddy has to go to the hospital," Susan explained. "But he can come later and visit you."

"At the toy store?" Emily questioned uncertainly.

"No, at my house." Susan was silently complimenting herself for her patience. "We'll go there after the toy store."

Emily pressed her face against her father's shoulder. "I don't want to go anywhere without Daddy," she insisted stubbornly.

"For goodness sakes, Dan," Susan muttered under her breath, "you're not being any help at all. I should think if you loved her so much, you'd try to make it easier for the child."

Dan looked up and found himself surrounded. Susan had been joined by her two attorneys and a pair of burly court officers. "I'm sorry, Doctor," one of them said, obviously unhappy with the task he had to perform, "but you heard the judge's decision. The little girl has to go with her mother. Better for her if you make her go than if we do."

"No!" Emily began to sob hysterically, clinging to her father. "Hold me, Daddy! Hold me!"

"I want to, honey, but I can't," Dan tried to explain, sure that he sounded like a traitor to his trusting little daughter. "Someday when you're a lot bigger, I hope you'll understand. I want to keep you as much as you want to stay, but I can't. . . ." His voice broke so that he didn't trust himself to say any more. All he could do was sit there helplessly as the officers pried Emily from his arms.

"I want to stay with my daddy! Please don't take me away!" Emily screamed.

"It will be fun for you, Em," Dan lied, "and I'll come to see you very often." At least he had unlimited visiting rights and he intended to exercise them every day, he promised himself.

Hearing his words, Susan gloated secretly. It was exactly what she wanted, frequent access to Dan.

"Will you come tomorrow?" Emily begged between convulsive sobs.

"Of course your daddy will," Susan answered for him. "He can come to visit you whenever he likes, every day if he wants to." She couldn't believe how perfectly her scheme was working. Whether he wanted it or not, she was about to become part of Dan's life again. Soon she'd be the most important part, she told herself confidently. He was angry with her now, but once he got over that, anything could happen, Susan thought.

If she were able to see into Dan's heart, though, she would not have been so pleased with herself. For if there had ever been a chance of winning back her former husband, Susan had just lost it. This time she had gone too far. She had alienated Dan deeply, absolutely, eternally. And nothing could ever make him forgive her.

Chapter Eight
Kissing and Telling

Lisa smoothed the sequined dinner dress over her trim figure and admired her reflection in the mirror. Grant was due at any moment with what she prayed was the long-awaited promise of a divorce. Hoping against hope, she'd put a bottle of vintage champagne on ice. The evening was cool for a midsummer night, and she shivered as she sprayed a mist of perfume on her bare shoulders. She wanted this to be a special night, a night of love and of promises that wouldn't be broken. And it could be, too, if Grant didn't let her down. Waiting was the worst of it, she thought nervously. She'd spent the day veering back and forth between glorious anticipation and sickening dread. Grant had to convince Joyce this time, he just had to.

"I won't think negatively. I won't think negatively," Lisa repeated to herself again and again. She was still telling herself the same thing an hour later when she heard the front door open.

Rushing to greet Grant, Lisa tried to put a rein on her excitement.

"Well, darling, how did it go?" she asked, reaching up to brush his cheek with a kiss.

He looked so tired and grim, she wasn't sure she wanted to hear his answer. But he patted his breast pocket and forced a smile. "I've got the papers right here, signed and sealed. Now we've just got to wait for the case to go through the courts."

"Terrific, darling," she gushed. "I knew you'd do it this time. I even put some champagne on ice to celebrate."

"Good. I could use a glass or, to be honest, the whole bottle," Grant admitted darkly. He'd gone to see Joyce with enough ammunition to wipe out all her arguments. It had been a painful ordeal. There wasn't a ploy that she didn't use, a game that she hadn't tried to play. And for what? That's what Grant couldn't understand. Why was she so desperate to preserve a marriage that had been over long ago? Possessiveness, even jealousy, were not motive enough.

"Was it really that bad?" Lisa's voice was soothing as she wrapped the chilled champagne bottle in an oversized damask napkin.

Grant listened to the cork pop before he

answered. "Let's put it this way, Lisa. Twisting Joyce's arm to get the divorce isn't something I'd ever want to do again."

"What happened?" she asked, filling two crystal glasses. Although she was burning with curiosity, she was careful not to show it.

"Nothing much really," Grant replied noncommittally. Even though there was nothing left to destroy between Joyce and him, he still felt uncomfortable revealing the pathetic little scene she had just played. Somehow he felt it would be disloyal, a betrayal of what Joyce and he had once shared, to tell Lisa.

Taking the glass she offered, Grant gulped the champagne like water, without even waiting for a toast.

"You weren't kidding about needing the whole bottle." Lisa laughed harshly. "Are you all right?"

"Never better," he insisted, taking the bottle from her. Grant filled his glass again and thought of Joyce. The first time he'd asked her for a divorce she'd succeeded in making him feel guilty. This time she'd tried hard to be provocative, to lure him back into her bed. Instead, she'd only been pitiful, so pitiful that he'd almost capitulated. But he had resisted, and she'd finally given in. Yet there was no sweetness in his victory. Joyce had been wearing a revealing summer dress intended for a girl half her age. Her makeup was too heavy, her perfume cloying. She'd never been like that when they were married.

But in her desperation, she'd tried to be something she wasn't. She'd tried to be blatantly appealing; she'd tried to be . . . Lisa.

The image was still vivid in his mind, and he shook his head to dispel the memory. The vision blurred, and Lisa was standing in front of him again, her glass raised, a bright smile on her lips.

"I propose a toast," she was saying. "To us, darling. May we always be so happy."

"To us," he echoed hollowly.

"Grant, are you sure you're okay?" she repeated, the concern clear in her eyes.

"I'm fine," he insisted.

She studied him intently. "Would it help if you talked about it?"

"I guess I drank the champagne too fast," he answered, brushing aside her question.

"Can I do anything . . . get you anything?" she asked, not convinced. At that moment Lisa was filled with a terrible dread. Had she won the battle against Joyce but lost the war? No, she told herself, it wasn't possible. It was just the champagne—it had to be.

Grant was staring at her intently, but his eyes revealed no emotion. "Just put your arms around me, Lisa," he murmured, "and hold me tight. That's what I need now." He had never spoken truer words. He needed Lisa's love, her desire, her fire to burn away the painful memories of Joyce.

"It's what I've been longing to do," Lisa

whispered thankfully. Taking the glass out of his hand, she brought his fingers to her lips and began to kiss each one. She knew better than to press Grant for an explanation. In the long run, it didn't matter what had passed between him and Joyce, Lisa told herself. The result was all that really mattered.

"I'm sorry you had to go through so much for me, darling," she said kissing his ring finger, which she planned very soon to encircle with a gold wedding band.

"At least I got what you wanted . . . what we both wanted," he answered softly.

So many hopes had been dashed, so many plans abandoned since Grant had first proposed that, even now, Lisa was reluctant to try again. And yet she wanted so much to set a firm wedding date at last. "I was thinking about an August wedding," she began tentatively.

Grant shook his head. "That would be pushing it, don't you think? We still have to wait until the divorce is final." He was calculating in his head. "Let's say October just to be on the safe side. I wouldn't want to be forced to postpone it again."

"Don't even think it," Lisa cried. "One more postponement and I'd begin to think that our marriage was jinxed before it had even begun."

Reaching out, Grant traced the line of her throat with his finger. "I never realized you were superstitious, Lisa."

"I'm not usually," she protested, though a sudden wave of fear shuddered through her. Suddenly October seemed very far away. There was so much time for something to go wrong.

"I'm going to love you tonight like you've never been loved before," Grant promised in a husky whisper. His hands caressed her body, shaping each contour to their demands.

For an instant, she found herself gazing at him with a haunting fear, trying to discover if he felt it too. Could a fate stronger than their desire, more powerful than love, be working against them? A frightening premonition of disaster swept through her before Grant's lips claimed hers and drove all thoughts and fears from her mind.

Kim Dixon turned down the stereo and listened to the insistent ring of the telephone. It was probably John, she thought unhappily. Kim didn't feel like talking to anyone, least of all her husband. In fact, she hadn't felt at all sociable since the night of their cocktail party for Dan Stewart.

Kim sighed deeply. The party had been a mistake from start to finish. She should never have allowed John to talk her into having it. Yet the temptation had been so great. Kim couldn't honestly say that she regretted it. How could she regret seeing a man like Dan again? How could any woman?

Dan! Although Kim knew she should have
resisted his kiss, it had been impossible. She
was still drawn to him irresistibly, like a miser
to gold. Dan was as solid, as genuine as gold.
She'd felt that the first time she'd met him.
How long ago had it been? Kim didn't like to
remember. It had been during one of the
lowest points in her life. Her sister, Jennifer,
had just died, and Kim had been on the verge
of divorcing John, sure that their marriage
had been a mistake from the first. Chasing
after her, he tripped and fell down the stairs.
At first, it had looked as if he would be
permanently paralyzed.

Kim still remembered the ambulance ride
to the hospital. She'd sat terrified beside
her unconscious husband. At that point all
thoughts of divorce were gone. How could
she walk out on a crippled husband? John had
married her when she'd been in trouble. Now
he was the one in need.

Maybe they could have patched their marriage back together, Kim thought, if Dan
hadn't come into their lives. But he'd been
John's doctor. Trying her best to be a dutiful
wife, Kim had conferred with him frequently
about her husband's condition, and each time
she'd found herself thinking more about the
doctor than about the patient. John's paralysis
had proven temporary, but by the time he'd
made a full recovery, Dan was living in
England. Now he was back, and the cocktail

party had proved beyond a shadow of a doubt that time had done nothing to mute her feelings for him.

The persistent ring of the telephone interrupted her thoughts, and she reached for the receiver reluctantly. "Dr. Dixon's residence," Kim answered automatically.

"Where have you been, Kim? I was just about to give up on you." Dan's strained, anxious voice shocked her into silence.

"Right here sitting beside the phone," she managed to answer.

"Can you meet me?"

"When?"

"Right now. It's important."

Kim heard the pleading note in his voice and felt it tug at her heart. Still she forced herself to refuse. "I don't think so, Dan. John will be—"

"Please, Kim," he begged. "I need you. I've lost Emily. I can't believe it." His voice broke.

"You mean the court . . ." Kim began.

"Yes. The case just ended. The judge awarded full custody to Susan with visiting rights for me. Please, Kim. I need to be with someone. Not someone," he corrected himself. "I need to be with you."

"I don't know, Dan," she began, knowing what would happen if she went to comfort him—what she wanted to happen. He sounded so distraught, so heartbroken. Kim could only imagine what it must feel like to lose a child. She knew firsthand how terrible it was to miscarry. How infinitely worse it must be to lose a child you'd loved and delighted in for four special years. Yet she didn't want to start an affair with Dan. Kim wasn't a sneak. She wanted an honest, open relationship. If there was going to be anything between her and Dan, she wanted it to be aboveboard. First she had to square things with her husband. John was so incredibly possessive.

"Will you meet me?" Dan begged. "All I want is to talk."

Is it? she wondered. She hoped he wanted more from her because she wanted infinitely more from him. "Dan," she began again tentatively.

A recorded voice broke in. "Please deposit five cents for an additional four minutes." Kim could hear Dan fumbling frantically for the change and swearing softly to himself.

"Where are you?" she asked.

"In a damned pay phone outside the courthouse, and I haven't got any more change. Listen, Kim, meet me as soon as you can at—"

The phone went dead in her hand. "Dan! Dan!" she called, pushing the button again and again, even though she knew they'd been disconnected. Putting down the receiver, she leaned back in her chair and stared up at the ceiling. At least she didn't have to make up her mind now, Kim thought disconsolately.

The decision had been taken out of her hands by the telephone company.

She hadn't rejected Dan, yet she hadn't deceived John either. Her conscience should feel clear, but it didn't. In the kitchen, she'd gone willingly, even eagerly, into his arms. Even though she'd known that John or any of the guests could have come into the kitchen at any moment she'd taken his kiss and answered it. His lips had been full, soft yet demanding. Kim had had the sensation of being drawn into a deep, fiery void that only their desire could fill. At the touch of his lips, so hungry yet at the same time so tender, she had felt as if he were breathing new life into her. It was as if she'd merely been existing during all the years she'd been married to John. But in Dan's arms, she could live with all the intensity, all the passion, all the sheer joy that had been absent from her life for so long. Was it just desire he aroused? Or was it something more, something deeper, more lasting, something so mysterious, so inexplicable, it could only be called love?

Now the man who had kissed her, the man who had brought her back to life with his lips, needed her. And she was turning a deaf ear. Turning her back on the possibility of happiness. Kim jumped up as if she'd been struck by lightning. What a fool she was and a coward besides! Without even stopping to run a comb through her hair, she grabbed the car keys and rushed out. Dan had to be somewhere near the courthouse, probably in some saloon drowning his sorrows. But no matter where he was and no matter how long it took, Kim was determined to find him.

A light drizzle began to fall as she pulled into the parking lot across from the court-house. It was a gentle summer rain, warm and light, and Kim found it oddly comforting as she started her search. In her hurry, she'd run out without an umbrella or a raincoat. The rain glistened on her face, made her hair curl and her thin, cotton blouse cling to her breasts. The downtown crowds began to thin. Although it was still light, the hour was growing late. Was it too late to find Dan? Kim wondered. He'd probably started home already to explain to his daughter Betsy why Emily wasn't going to be living with them any longer, she told herself, but something drove her on.

Kim must have searched a dozen bars before she finally found him, hunched over a table in a corner booth, nursing a bourbon and soda.

"Dan," Kim said softly. "I thought I'd never find you." An intense feeling of relief swept over her, and for an instant she felt almost light-headed.

He stared at her, not trusting his eyes or his voice. "You're drenched, Kim," he said husk-ily.

"A little rain never hurt anyone." She brushed aside his concern and slid into the booth beside him.

"Do you want a drink?"

She shook her head. "No, are you all right?"

He shrugged. "I don't know what that means anymore. I still hurt all over if that's an answer. I suppose I always will."

"Tell me what happened," she urged, studying the pain that was so clearly etched on his handsome face.

"I lost Emily. That's about all there is to tell. The whole proceeding was very efficient, very judicial, and thoroughly barbaric," he added bitterly.

"When can you see her?" Kim asked, hoping that the anticipation of seeing his daughter would lighten his heart.

"Tomorrow. I promised Emily I would. It was the only way she would go with Susan." Dan bit his lip to hold back his tears. Ever since he could remember, he'd been told it was unmanly to cry. He couldn't let his emotions loose now even in front of Kim.

"It must have been terrible, Dan." She touched his sleeve tenderly, a gesture of sympathy that said more than mere words.

"It was," he answered simply. "Worse than anything—even Liz's death. The bailiff had to pull Emily from my arms. She was clinging to me with every ounce of strength she had, and she was sobbing." He buried his head in his hands, hearing his daughter's small, frightened voice again, the voice that would ring in his heart as long as he lived. He felt that he had let Emily down. He should have stayed in England instead of taking a chance with his little girl's happiness.

"How could the judge be so cruel?" Kim exclaimed. "Couldn't he see what Emily wanted?"

"In the eyes of the court, I'm a criminal. I kidnapped my own baby from her mother. All the judge was doing was returning property to its rightful owner," Dan added bitterly. "Didn't you know? Fathers have no rights, just financial obligations. They don't love their children as much as mothers do—at least they're not supposed to in our society."

"That's ridiculous."

He laughed harshly. "Believe me, no one knows that better than I do. But I didn't stand a chance in there. I knew when I came back from England that I was taking a risk, but I didn't realize how big a one."

"At least you'll see Emily tomorrow," Kim said, trying her best to console him.

"Susan said to come over anytime, every day, if I want to."

"Well, that was decent of her," Kim admitted grudgingly.

Dan shrugged and took a gulp of the bourbon. The ice had melted and the soda water had lost its fizz. "I wouldn't be so sure . . . not with Susan. I know her too well. She doesn't really want Emily. She never wanted children. They interfere with her career. She just had Emily to keep me from walking out on her, and I'm sure that she's only taking her now to get even."

"I know Susan would like to get you back. John has told me as much," Kim said quietly. "But do you really believe she's that vindictive?"

"You know something, Kim," he answered, feeling suddenly more tired and defeated than he had ever felt in his life. "I don't give a damn what Susan is. I just care about Emily, and nothing in the world can make me believe she's going to be happier living with her mother."

"Well, whatever Susan's motives, you can see Emily every day. That's something," Kim reminded him, hoping to lighten his gloom.

"Terrific, isn't it? Visiting rights! I'm allowed to pay a call on my own daughter."

"It's better than nothing."

"Is it?" Dan shook his head hopelessly. "I don't know if I can even go through with it. I can't stand the thought of someone having to pull her out of my arms again. I'm not even sure I could go alone, at least on the first day." He looked up at Kim with silent, pleading eyes. "Will you come with me?"

"To Susan's?" Kim asked, shocked at the request. It was the last place in the world she wanted to go. "I don't think my presence would exactly soothe the troubled waters."

"I don't mean come in with me," he assured her, "just ride over. No one will see you and I need moral support."

"If you really want me to, Dan," she agreed reluctantly.

"I really do." His eyes met hers, frank and direct and full of longing. Putting a powerful arm around her, Dan drew Kim against his body. "Come on," he said, his voice thick with emotion. "I'd better get you home before you catch pneumonia."

She looked up at him. "It would be worth it," she murmured.

"Nothing would be worth that," he insisted.

Kim smiled through the tears that clouded her eyes. "Finding you again is."

Chapter Nine
Dear John

A sudden storm swept into Oakdale with hurricane force. Just moments before the day had been clear blue, perfect for a lazy picnic or a lunch by the country club pool.

Tom Hughes peered out the window, a worried expression on his narrow face, and watched the rain fall. It beat like a percussion band on the hood of his new Toyota and crushed the gold and amber nasturtiums that Carol had planted along the edge of the driveway.

"Damn!" he muttered under his breath. All his plans would have to be changed. The table for three he'd reserved by the club pool would be a bathtub by now, and eating in the formal dining room was always so stiff. It was not at all the atmosphere he wanted for introducing Natalie to his mother. Lisa was already so wary of her, Tom wanted their first meeting to be as easy and relaxed as possible.

A streak of lightning cut through the blanket of black clouds. Maybe he could catch his mother before she started out, he thought with a glimmer of hope. They could have lunch another day, and he and Natalie could spend the rainy afternoon creating their own summer storm. Warming at the thought, he dialed Lisa and held the receiver, listening to the telephone ring a dozen times.

"Damn," Tom swore again. "Damn, damn, damn." Lisa must have started out before the storm broke. She was always so punctual, unlike Natalie who usually waited until she was supposed to be someplace to start getting ready. Nothing was working out the way he'd planned. His mother would probably be angry because her hair frizzed in the rain, and the longer they kept her waiting, the madder she'd grow. And Natalie, where was Natalie?

The week before when Tom had arranged the date, she had promised to be standing on his front doorstep at the stroke of twelve. But he hadn't been able to reach her in over an hour, and it was almost twelve-thirty. Tom had been so busy himself, wrapping up as many cases as he could to clear the decks for his honeymoon, that he hadn't had time to wonder what had happened to his bride to be. He'd just assumed she was getting herself ready for their wedding.

Natalie was so different from Carol, he mused. The only part of the wedding that seemed to interest her at all was what she'd wear and how she'd look. She didn't want to have anything to do with the actual arrangements. Since her family didn't live in Oakdale, Lisa had offered to give the wedding, and Natalie had accepted readily—too readily, it seemed to Tom. It was unnatural not to take more of an interest in your own wedding, he thought as he checked his watch again.

Quarter-to-one. Lisa would be steaming. He'd have to call the club and say his car stalled in the rain. Then he'd have to try to call Natalie again. It would be quicker now if he stopped by her apartment and picked her up. Tom was just starting to dial when he saw a mail truck pull into the driveway behind his car and the driver dart up to the door.

The man was dripping like a fountain. "Special delivery for Thomas Hughes." He pulled a letter out of his pouch. "Sign here, please," he said, indicating a blank space marked with an X on the form attached to the letter.

A nervous client, Tom thought with annoyance as he closed the door. Going back to the phone, he dialed Natalie's number again and tore the letter open as he listened to it ring. When he began to read, though, he dropped the receiver back into the cradle with a thud.

"No! No, Natalie, you can't do this to

me," he muttered through clenched teeth. He slammed his fist down on the table, pinning the letter beneath it. Then sinking down into the chair, he began to read again, slowly, haltingly, as if each word was impossible to believe.

Dear Tom,

By the time you get this letter, I will be far from Oakdale so there is no point in trying to find me—and believe me, you are better off without me. I should have refused when you proposed to me, but I didn't have the courage. I wanted to be the Natalie you believe I am. But the real me is not good enough to be your wife. The mistakes I've made in the past, the sins I've committed, have made me unworthy of a man like you. That's why I can't go through with our wedding.

I know I haven't been fair to you, Tom, but I hope you'll find it in your heart to forgive me, and try to remember the wonderful times we shared.

Yours always,
Natalie

Tom put his head down on the table and covered his face, imagining Natalie alone in a town she didn't know with no friends, no job, no one to turn to. If only she'd talked to him honestly and openly instead of running away, he thought miserably. But the truth was far different from Tom's thoughts.

At that very moment Natalie was combing her fingers through the golden-red hair that covered Luke Porter's massive chest.

"It's good to have you back, hon," Luke mumbled, ruffling her hair with a beefy hand. "You're as hungry as you ever were, aren't you?" He laughed, a rumble that started deep in his chest.

Natalie licked her lips. She'd been back in Kilborn for two days and two nights, and almost every hour of it she'd spent in bed with Luke. For an instant she remembered Tom. He was good, but he'd never be Luke. Powerful, rough, demanding, Luke Porter was the only man she couldn't twist around her little finger and the only man who could satisfy her darkest desires. They were two of a kind, she and Luke. That's why she'd run out on Tom, to give Luke one last chance. What a pair they would make, if only he would finally marry her.

"You still don't understand, Luke," she murmured. "I'm hungry for *you*. You're the only man I'll ever love. How can I make you believe that?"

"You don't have to. I already believe you."

"Then what are you going to do about it?" she pressed.

"What do you think? I'll be here when you want to play," he promised.

"But that's not all I want," Natalie whispered breathily. "I love you. I want to marry you."

"Come on, hon, get off it," he said, a trace of annoyance in his tone. "You're about ten years too late. I've got a wife already, remember?"

"But you don't love her," Natalie persisted.

"I don't love you, either," Luke admitted harshly. "But that doesn't mean I'm going to kick you out of my bed."

Natalie stopped as still as a statue and stared down at him, feeling the pain of rejection like a stab wound. "That's not true, Luke. I know you love me," she insisted. "You're just too lazy to get a divorce." But even as she pleaded, Luke was shaking his head. When Natalie came back to him, he thought they could just pick up where they'd left off when she moved to Oakdale. But now it was clear that she was going to be a royal pain. Women were all alike. They all wanted love and marriage when all he was out for was a good time. He had all the rest, a home, a wife, a couple of kids.

"I don't love you, Natalie. I just think you're a first-rate lover. Maybe the best I've ever had," he added.

"I hate you!" she spat back at him, rolling away from his reach and scrambling out of bed. "I gave up a wedding to come back here to you. Don't you understand that?"

A cruel smile played at the corners of Luke's lips. "No one asked you to, honey, least of all me."

"You'll be sorry, Luke," Natalie swore, pulling on her clothes as fiercely as if she were dressing for battle. "Because this time, when I walk out of here, I'm never coming back, even if you get down on your knees and beg."

Linking his hands behind his head, Luke watched her dress. "You'll come back, honey, the minute I snap my fingers. Believe me, you will," he said with supreme confidence. "You can't keep away from me, Natalie, because nobody makes love to you the way I do."

"Dream on, lover boy," she snapped bitterly.

This time, Luke was wrong. No matter how much she loved him, Natalie would never come back. If she couldn't have what she wanted now, she'd settle for second best. The bus schedule to Oakdale was stuffed in her purse with enough cash for a one-way ticket back.

As she wriggled into her slacks, Natalie was already composing the speech she'd make to Tom. "I couldn't stay away, Tom. I know I should have for your sake. And I tried. Honestly, I did. But I love you so much, I had to see you again. I wanted to touch you, hold you and kiss you just one more time. Just once, Tom, just once . . ."

Natalie wore a very private, very secret smile as she prepared to walk out of Luke's life. All she had to do was get Tom back. Then she could make him do anything she wanted. It would be as easy as taking candy from a baby, she thought smugly.

Tossing her bag over her shoulder, Natalie looked back one last time at the man lying naked in the rumpled sheets. "This time next month, I'll be Mrs. Thomas Hughes," she said with supreme satisfaction. "Then you can eat your heart out, Luke Porter."

"It's so much easier, when you come with me. I don't know why," Dan admitted, slipping his hand into Kim's.

"Let's not even think about it, at least not yet." She smiled at him in the dim evening light. "We don't want to spoil a good thing."

He laughed softly and took her in his arms. "I don't think we could—not this time," he said, holding her longer than he knew he should. Emily would be waiting for him. His heart ached when he thought of her sad, despairing eyes. She couldn't understand why he would never take her home with him. If anything, he loved her more fiercely because she'd been taken away from him, but he couldn't make her understand that. Every visit ended in the same heart-wrenching way. Locking her plump little arms around his neck, she'd cling to him until finally he was forced to break her hold, and when he turned to leave, her question would follow him. "Don't you love me anymore, Daddy?"

Closing his eyes tight, Dan hugged Kim as fiercely as Emily hugged him. "I don't know how much longer I can take these visits. I keep hoping Susan will get tired of the whole charade and give Emily back, but she's so stubborn. She's there every minute trying to come between Emily and me. She acts as if I came to see her and Emily is only getting in the way."

"You've got to hang in there, Dan, for Emily." Kim tried to give him courage. But there wasn't anything she could do except be there as often as she could for him.

Ever since his first visit, Kim had tried to go with Dan or at least meet him discreetly down the street from Susan's house. It seemed to mean so much to him, and it brought them a special closeness which she wouldn't trade for anything.

But Kim couldn't make it every night. It was difficult to think of fresh excuses to slip away for an hour, especially on John's days off. How could she explain, even to herself, the powerful bond that was growing between Dan and herself with every passing day. Except for these surreptitious visits to Susan's house, she had scarcely ever been alone with him. Yet she felt that she had never been more intimate with any man.

What did she mean to Dan? Did he consider her a friend, a confidant, a sympathetic shoulder to cry on, or something more? He never said, and she never pressed him, knowing that for now at least, his deepest emotions were entangled in his concern for Emily. What did Dan mean to her? Kim didn't hesitate with that answer. He meant everything. Although she hated sneaking behind her husband's back, she knew Dan needed her more than John did. And they were always very careful to make sure no one saw them. Kim didn't want anyone else telling John. When the time was right, she would talk to him herself.

"Give Emily a hug for me," she said, trying to break away from his arms.

"A hug and a kiss," he whispered back against her moist lips, and then in the shadows, he was kissing her, and she was kissing him, giving in to the temptation neither one could resist any longer, oblivious to the delicate hand that pulled the curtains of her bedroom window open a crack and the eyes that glared angrily, jealously through the twilight at them.

Susan had been waiting for Dan—but for Dan alone.

"Shouldn't you be home with Emily? I thought once you got the child from Dan, you were going to cut back on the hours you keep."

"I have. I'm on my way home," she insisted, glancing at her watch, "just as soon as I get the results of this test. It's really exciting."

"Susan," John interrupted in disbelief. "I know you've gotten a good housekeeper for the kid, but just how late do you expect the woman to stay?"

"Oh, she's leaving at five-thirty today," Susan answered with a total lack of concern. "Some family nonsense. If it's not one excuse, it's another."

"It's five-thirty now." John tapped at the crystal of his watch. "What are you doing hanging around here?"

"Get off my back, John," Susan snapped. "I'm leaving in fifteen minutes."

"But who's at home with Emily now?" he persisted.

"Nobody," she almost screamed in exasperation. You'd think the sun had to rise and set on a four-year-old. He sounded just like Dan. "I told the housekeeper to just take off if I wasn't there because I'd definitely be on my way and she was making such a big deal about leaving at the stroke of half past five."

"Well, I don't know much about kids," John admitted. "But it seems to me that Emily is too young to be left in a house alone. What if something happens? What will you tell Dan?"

"Oh, you're such a worrier, John," Susan sighed. "Nothing's going to happen to Emily. I know my own daughter. She's very mature and independent for her age."

"She's going to have to be with a mother like you," John said skeptically.

But Susan only laughed. "The way I look at it, Emily has survived four years without a mother. She'll last another half an hour."

John walked away, shaking his head. "Maybe so, Susan, but she had a father then," he called back in warning.

John Dixon's words returned to her an hour or so later as she sank back in a refreshingly cool tub and thought about her daughter. Susan hadn't been entirely honest with John. The truth was she'd gone back to her old hours at the hospital because she had neither the desire nor the interest in spending time with her daughter. Maybe she was too old, too settled in her career to start mothering a four-year-old. On the other hand, Susan told herself, eager to shift the blame, Emily might simply be a difficult child. She was very uncommunicative.

Susan was thoroughly disgusted with her daughter. She'd expected Emily to adjust to her new home by the end of the summer. Instead the child seemed more withdrawn and unfriendly every day. When she'd finally arrived home, Susan had found Emily in her room. Although there were enough dolls and stuffed animals and games to fill a toy store, the child was hunched in a corner with an old blanket wrapped around her knees.

The instant she saw her mother, Emily brightened. "May I call my daddy, please?" she had asked hopefully.

Susan rolled her eyes to the ceiling, stifling the urge to shake the kid. "You might say hello Mommy, when I come home," she said crisply. "And the answer is no, you may not call your father."

Emily's eyes filled with tears. "But I have something to tell him," she insisted. "A secret."

"Emily," Susan answered sharply. "There are no secrets in this house. Do you understand? Now why don't you stop moping and play with some of these toys. What did I buy them for if you never touch them?"

"Will you play with me, Mommy?" Emily brightened again.

"Not now, dear." Susan frowned in annoyance. "Mommy is too tired now."

"Then may I call my daddy?"

"Damn it," Susan muttered under her breath. Emily was going to begin crying any second. If there was one thing Susan hated, it was Emily's tears. The little girl seemed to cry constantly. Obviously, Dan had spoiled the kid, she thought. But she wasn't going to make the same mistake.

"Listen, Emily," she began again with false brightness. "You play for a little while. Mommy's going to take a bath because she's so hot and tired, then we'll have supper, and then Daddy will be coming to see you," she promised.

The only time Susan cared about being home with Emily was in the evenings because

Dan usually came to visit after he closed the office. Ever since she saw him with Kim, though, the visits had become nerve wracking.

Susan shut her eyes and let the bath water lap around her breasts. She was petrified that she was losing ground with Dan. He was as impossible as Emily, barely acknowledging her existence when he came to visit. And now it seemed that he was beginning a relationship with Kim. The embrace she had witnessed rankled unpleasantly. Had they kissed in the shadows beneath her window? Susan wasn't even sure she wanted to know.

She was still preoccupied with the question when, wrapped in a terry cloth robe, she walked into Emily's room. It was exactly as it had been when she got home except for one detail. The corner where Emily had been was empty.

Checking her annoyance, Susan called brightly, "Emily, dear, come on down and help me get supper." She waited impatiently, then tried again. And again she received no response. With an unspoken curse, she began to hunt for the child under the bed, in the closets and the bathroom. "Emily!" she called again and again at the top of her lungs as she went downstairs.

Susan searched each room, looked out in the yard, but there was no sign of Emily. When a child is too quiet, it's usually a sign of mischief, she reminded herself. Emily must have gotten into trouble, and now she was hiding. "Come on out, Emily," she called in her sweetest voice. "Whatever you did, Mommy won't be mad with you."

Susan waited and waited with mounting impatience. "Damn it," she swore angrily. "Come out this minute, Emily Stewart, or I'm going to give you a spanking you'll never forget."

Both the promise and the threat were wasted, though, because Emily couldn't hear either one. She'd waited for her mother to finish her bath until she couldn't bear to wait any longer. Emily wanted someone to play with. She wanted Betsy and her father, and she wanted them now, not late at night when she was half asleep.

Still wrapped in her comforting old blanket, she tiptoed downstairs and trotted bravely down the street, confident that she could remember the way back to her father's house.

Chapter Ten
Lost and Found

Waving at the house where she'd been so lonesome, Emily trotted down the street as fast as her little legs would carry her. She was singing happily to herself as she turned the corner looking for her father's yellow house. Although she knew she wasn't allowed to cross the street alone, Emily looked all around, and when she was satisfied that no adult was watching, she darted across. A woman, seeing she was alone, pulled over in her car.

"What are you doing out by yourself, little girl?" she asked. "Where's your mommy?"

"My daddy," Emily corrected firmly.

"Well, where's your daddy? I don't see him," the woman said.

Looking up at her with serious eyes, Emily

explained patiently. "You don't understand. I'm going home to my daddy. He lives in a yellow house." She seemed so confident, so sure of what she was doing and where she was going, that the woman shrugged in resignation. Muttering to herself how irresponsible parents were these days, she drove away.

Emily had sung every song she knew, and still she hadn't found the yellow house where Betsy and her daddy lived. The sky was growing darker and darker, and the trees and bushes she passed seemed to change right in front of her eyes to huge black monsters. Emily was getting tired, hungry, and scared. She'd never been out after dark before by herself. And soon, she thought, it would be too dark to see the color of the houses. How would she find her daddy then?

Sticking out her tongue, she caught the wet, salty tears that were beginning to spill down her cheeks. Maybe she should go back. Her mother would be mad at her for running away, but that couldn't be much worse than being alone in the dark. When Emily turned around though, she couldn't remember which way she had come. Everything looked so different at night.

"Daddy, Daddy," she sobbed. But she knew her father couldn't hear her. What if she never found him again . . . or Betsy . . . or even her mother. Crumbling into a little frightened ball, Emily sat down on the curb, her knees pulled up tight against her chest, and cried. If only she'd brought Amanda with her, she wouldn't be so scared. Her mother insisted that Amanda was only a doll and refused to set a place for her at dinner, but Emily knew better. That's why she'd helped Amanda hide when they heard Susan come home. Amanda always wanted to hide when Emily's mother came home. Now though Emily wished she had Amanda in her arms.

"This is no place for a little girl to be sleeping."

Emily blinked. She didn't remember falling asleep but she hadn't seen the brown panel truck drive up or the man get out. Although he looked spooky with his long hair and rough, unshaven face, his voice sounded kind. "Well, at least you're awake now," he said and smiled.

Emily closed her eyes again so she wouldn't have to look at him. She felt safer just listening to his voice.

"Where do you live?" he asked.

Shaking her head, she began to cry again. "I don't know," she sobbed. "I want to go home to my daddy."

"Come on, don't cry on me." He gave her shoulder a gentle shake. "My name's Hank, what's yours?"

"Emily." She sniffled, beginning to hope that maybe Hank could help her. At least she didn't feel so frightened anymore, but she still kept her eyes tightly shut.

"Okay. Emily, come on with me like a

good girl and maybe we'll find your daddy."
He swung her up into his arms as if she were
weightless.

"Can you, please?" Emily opened one eye a
crack and begged.

"I'm not making any promises, but you
can't sit here in the gutter all night." Hank
said gruffly.

Before Emily realized what was happening,
he had carried her to an abandoned truck,
opened the back door and tossed her inside.
"You'll sleep better here. There's a blanket in
the corner, if you're cold. I've spent many a
night in here. You'll be fine," he said.

"I want to get out," Emily cried. But it was
too late. Hank was already closing the doors,
plunging her into a darkness even blacker
than the night.

Dan Stewart closed the door of his examining
room and went back into his office, taking off
his white coat as he walked. Emergency
surgery at noon had thrown off his appoint-
ment schedule. It was after nine, and he'd just
finished with his last patient. Emily would be
waiting for him, big eyes glued to the win-
dowpane watching, wondering why he hadn't
come.

Sitting down at the desk with a deep sigh,
Dan flipped through a stack of telephone
messages. By the time he finished answering
all his calls, it would be another hour anyway.

Emily would probably be asleep by then. He rubbed his eyes, physically and emotionally exhausted. How do you tell a four-year-old that she has to wait for her father's love until after he has taken care of a lot of very sick people?

Dan had tried to explain things many times to Emily, but he never felt that she understood a word he was saying. To her it was so simple: I love you. I want to be with you always. Trying hard not to let his guilt over Emily distract him now, Dan read the first message and reached for the phone to place a call. But before he could dial, the telephone rang and Susan's frantic voice wiped away every other concern.

"Dan! I'm so glad I caught you. Something terrible's happened. I can't find Emily anyplace. I've searched the house and the yard and . . . Dan, I'm so worried."

"Hold on a minute, Susan," he said. "It's not going to do anyone any good if you get hysterical. Now start at the beginning and tell me exactly what happened. Where did you last see Emily?"

"In her room." Susan choked back a frightened sob. "I told her to play there while I took a bath, then we'd go downstairs and have supper together. But when I went to get her, she wasn't there. She's not anywhere." Susan's voice began to rise to a hysterical pitch again.

"What time was that?" Dan cut in sharply. "What time did you see her playing in her room?"

"Around six or six-thirty," Susan admitted.

"Six or six-thirty?" Dan shouted incredulously. "That was three hours ago. What the hell have you been doing since then?"

"Going out of my mind with worry over her!" Susan screamed back. "I've been looking everywhere I can think of and calling everyone."

"What did the police say?"

"The police?" Susan couldn't disguise the fear in her voice. "What do the police have to do with this?"

Gritting his teeth to hold back his fury, Dan said, "If someone finds a lost child, she is usually taken to the nearest police station, Susan."

"But I don't want to get the police involved in this. That's why I called you," she insisted.

"It certainly took you long enough to dial this number," he answered grimly. "God only knows what may have happened to her in three hours."

"I just can't believe Emily is lost. She was right here in her room," Susan kept repeating. "She's got to be hiding someplace— unless . . . unless . . . Dan, you didn't come over here while I was in the bath and take her, did you?"

The fury that Dan had been holding back for his lost daughter's sake exploded. "Do you think I would play games with Emily?" he shouted. "That's your style, Susan, not mine."

Susan could almost feel the heat of his anger through the telephone and she began to make a quick retreat. "Well, it's not unheard of," she whined defensively. "You read in the paper every day about fathers kidnapping their own children. And you did do it once. You did take Emily away to England."

"This isn't the time to start raking up the past," he fumed. "You just sit right where you are, Susan, and don't move for anyone or anything. I'm going to find Emily, and when I do, believe me, I'm going to drag you back into that courtroom and have you declared an unfit mother."

"But I didn't do anything," Susan protested.

"That's just it. You didn't do anything for Emily. That's probably why she ran away."

"You don't know she ran away, Dan. You're only guessing."

"When a kid is missing for three hours, it's a pretty educated guess," he snapped back. "You took Emily away from me, but once you got her, you didn't know what to do with her. You never wanted her, you just wanted to get back at me. Well, be happy, Susan, because now you have. I'm going out to look for Emily now, and if anything's happened to her, you're going to wish you were never born."

Slamming down the receiver, Dan bit his

lip to keep from crying and dialed the emergency police number. After answering what seemed like endless questions, he called Kim. Just the sound of her voice calmed him. Although it was filled with concern, he could hear hope in it, too. In a few moments he felt reassured that Emily would be found. When Kim said that she and John would join the search and would ask their neighbors to look for Emily, too. Dan felt encouraged. As long as Kim was looking, they were together, and together they would find Emily. They had to find her.

"You look as though you just saw a ghost," John said when his wife finished talking.

"That was Dan Stewart," Kim answered, trying to keep her voice from shaking. "His daughter, Emily ran away from Susan's house. He's trying to get everyone he knows to join the search for the child."

The instant he heard the news, John remembered his conversation with Susan that afternoon, but he didn't tell Kim about it. Susan must feel guilty enough, he thought as he went to get flashlights for the search. He was so preoccupied with the memory of that ominous conversation that he didn't notice how tense Kim was as they started out.

Before midnight, half the town of Oakdale was out looking for Emily Stewart. The local radio and TV stations were broadcasting a description of the little girl and giving a special emergency number to call with any

information on the lost child. Four police
units with specially trained dogs had been
mobilized and Dan had an ambulance standing by in case Emily was hurt. In the space of
three hours, he looked as if he had aged ten
years. Although he had blamed Susan on the
phone, in his heart he blamed himself as well.
Emily must have been waiting for him, waiting and waiting until she'd given up and gone
out to look for him. He should have called to
tell her that he'd be very late, but he'd been
so busy, he hadn't wanted to take the time.
More than that, he admitted with a lump in
his throat, he had been afraid she might begin
to cry on the phone, and he hadn't wanted to
know he'd disappointed her.

The search seemed hopeless. Although it
had begun at Susan's house and spread out in
every direction that Emily might have taken,
not a single clue was found. A woman called
the radio station to say that she'd spotted a
child alone on the street around seven
o'clock. If Susan had reported Emily missing
immediately, it might have helped, but now
it was just one more bit of useless information.

The searchers had covered miles. Their
feet ached, and their hopes sagged. The
police sergeant mobilizing the investigation
warned Dan that there was little point in
continuing any longer. A four-year-old child
could never walk the miles they had combed.
There were only two alternatives left to them.

Either she was in one of the houses in the area or a driver had picked her up. In the morning, the police would go to court to get authorization to conduct a house-to-house search. In the meantime, a bulletin went out alerting all cars to be on the lookout for a four-year-old girl fitting Emily's description.

The first orchid hues of morning were lightening the sky. Reluctantly, Dan agreed with the sergeant. There was no point in searching any longer. He began to go from friend to friend, thanking each person with a silent handshake. He couldn't trust his voice to speak, but the emotion in his face said volumes. Some of the searchers were crying as they began to turn back for home, Kim among them. She wanted to be with Dan, but John was putting his arm around her shoulders, drawing her away from the crowd.

Suddenly she stopped and listened intently. The sergeant's radio was crackling a message. Everyone crowded in to hear the excited voice. Miles away on the other side of town, a team of dogs had picked up Emily's scent around an abandoned brown panel truck parked in a vacant lot. The searchers began to cheer and hug each other as news that the child had been found spread among them.

"Can I talk to her?" Dan asked the sergeant huskily.

He raised an eyebrow skeptically. "You can try, Doctor, but don't be disappointed if she doesn't answer. My officers say she appears to be in a state of shock. When they jimmied the door of the truck, they found her cowering in a corner too frightened to even get out."

Dan was trembling as he took the walkie-talkie and started to talk. "Emily it's Daddy," he said, swallowing hard. "I love you, and I'm coming to get you right now."

For what seemed like an infinite moment, the only sound was the static of the radio. Then a little girl's voice came through loud and clear. "Daddy! Daddy! I love you."

The Oakdale courtroom was just as Dan remembered it, only this time he felt confident, even buoyant. Once Emily had been found, he didn't waste any time filing a petition to have her removed from her mother's custody and returned to him. Glancing across the aisle as the judge entered, he saw that Susan wasn't even attending. Her lawyers sat alone, looking grim.

Although he was still furious when he thought of how Susan had jeopardized Emily's safety, he had no desire to punish her for it. He just wanted to get his daughter back, back where she would be secure and well cared for and loved one day soon by a new mother. Susan simply wasn't cut out for motherhood, and, in spite of their blood ties, Emily was virtually a stranger to her, an alien living in her house. What did Susan know about children? What interest did she have in their irrational fears and inconsequential concerns? The white mice in the research lab were more like her children than Emily, Dan thought. He only hoped that the child hadn't been permanently emotionally scarred by the ordeal she'd suffered.

Kim didn't have any first-hand experience with children either. Still Dan was sure that she'd be a wonderful mother. Was that just what he wanted to believe or did he see some quality in Kim that he had never seen in Susan? Dan wondered. But he didn't have a chance to settle the question in his own mind. The judge was entering—the same judge who had ordered him to give up Emily. Now he thought bitterly that the man was going to be forced to eat his words.

The proceedings were quick and painless this time. The policeman who found Emily was the only witness called. But his testimony was so damning, Dan thought, that Susan would definitely be declared an unfit mother this time. The judge's voice, asking if her lawyers were prepared to present any defense, brought his attention back to the proceedings. The older of the two attorneys stood up and approached the bench.

"If it please the court," he began, clearing his throat self-consciously, "Dr. Susan Stewart on advice of her physician, John Dixon, is unable to attend today's hearing. She is still suffering from shock caused by the disappearance of her daughter. Therefore, I respectfully request a postponement until such time as she is able to attend."

Chris Hughes glanced at Dan, who gave a curt nod. "I object." The attorney jumped up. "The issue facing this court is not Susan Stewart's condition but the shock that the child has sustained due to her mother's negligence."

"Objection sustained," the judge said brusquely. "Postponement denied. Is the defense prepared to call its first witness?"

"There will be no witnesses, your honor," the attorney said, "but I would like an opportunity to correct the allegation that has been made here today. Contrary to the testimony that has been given, Susan Stewart is a loving and devoted mother. Since the court granted her custody, she has always put the interest and well-being of her daughter above her own. But I should remind the court that Dr. Stewart has a very vital and important position in this community as a chief medical researcher in Memorial Hospital. At considerable hardship to herself, Dr. Stewart arranged her schedule so that she would be free to assume the primary care of her daughter. However, like so many other professional parents, she did entrust secondary care to a housekeeper. The woman was highly recommended as a responsible, experienced caretaker for children. Unfortunately, she did not live up to her responsibility.

"I submit to the court that the incident

which brings us before you today—unfortunate though it is—could have happened in any family where the parents are both professionals. In no way was it caused by a mother's neglect as has been charged here today. Therefore, I ask the court to dismiss the case without further delay and order Emily Stewart returned to her rightful home. It would be an even greater tragedy if, just now, when the child is beginning to form a close bond with her mother, she is separated again. I don't need to remind the court that nothing, and no one, can make up for the loss of a mother's loving care."

Dan stared at the attorney unable to believe what he had just heard. "Chris," he said angrily to his own lawyer, "that's a damned lie. Emily didn't run away from some careless babysitter. She wandered away while her mother was right there in the house. Susan admitted that herself when she called me."

"Calm down, Dan." Chris put a reassuring hand on his arm. "Or you'll give yourself a heart attack. I know the facts as well as you," he murmured as he rose to set the record straight. "Objection, your honor. The facts of the case are clear in the police report Susan Stewart herself made on the night of the child's disappearance. That is marked exhibit number two."

Riffling through the papers in front of him, the judge squinted over his glasses. "Objection sustained."

Dan listened intently to the rest of the exchange between the two lawyers. But it seemed to him that the outcome of the case hinged on a single question: Would the judge have the courage to admit that he'd made a mistake in the first place?

The court recessed for lunch, but Dan had no appetite. The hour-long break seemed to stretch for days. Although Chris Hughes invited him to lunch, Dan refused. He was too tense to sit in a restaurant. Instead he walked through downtown Oakdale, window-shopping without seeing a thing. When everyone finally reconvened in the court-room, the judge took off his glasses and stared at the empty spot directly between the two counsels' tables. He was a distinguished man with salt-and-pepper hair and refined, even haughty, features. Yet he looked distinctly embarrassed, Dan thought. Or was it wishful thinking on his part?

Avoiding looking directly at anyone, the judge gave his decision. Reversing his previous judgment, he returned Emily to her father permanently. Susan was denied visiting rights until Emily recovered fully from the trauma she had suffered, and even then they were restricted.

Listening to the decision, Dan felt no flush of victory, only a deep sadness. Susan was an intelligent, ambitious woman with a satisfying career. Her life was far from empty, and yet he was sure that one day she would wake up and realize how much joy and fulfillment she had thrown away by ignoring Emily.

Dan was glad he wouldn't be there to witness that day. When it came, Susan would be a broken woman.

The summer light was deceptive. Susan knew it must be later than it appeared as she looked out on the still-bright day. Dan's housekeeper would be ringing the doorbell any moment to pick up Emily's things. Susan knew she should go upstairs and pack them, but the house was too quiet. The silence was driving her crazy, and it was just the beginning. That was the worst of it.

Looking up at the kitchen clock, she went to the bar and fixed herself a scotch on the rocks. It was five o'clock, the cocktail hour. It felt more like five A.M. The day had seemed interminable. First she had to endure the nerve-wracking wait for her lawyer's call, then the crushing decision, now the emptiness that seemed infinite. Susan knew the night would be even longer. She hadn't just lost Emily, she'd lost Dan, and nothing would ever bring him back.

She had no family left now, no hope of any. All the time that Dan had been in England, Susan had never given up hope. One day he'd come home to Oakdale, she'd always known, and when he did, she would be waiting. There was nothing left to wait for any longer.

Swallowing the scotch in a long gulp that

burned her throat, she filled the glass again and carried it with her as she wandered from room to room. The house looked just the way it had when Dan had lived there. She'd never wanted to change it. Now she wished she'd thrown away everything that had reminded her of him. Dan was right. She should have started a fresh life after their divorce instead of clinging to an impossible dream. It was too late for that now, she thought, draining the tumbler again.

Going back to the kitchen, Susan was about to put the glass in the sink, but she thought better of it and decided to have another drink. Three drinks aren't too much, she told herself, filling the tumbler with scotch. The third time she didn't bother with the ice. It was too much trouble to wrestle with the frozen trays, and there was an annoying buzzing, like a broken alarm clock, in her head. Swallowing the fresh drink seemed to deaden the sound.

Everything was beginning to fade, she thought with relief, the disappointment, the bitterness, the heartache. Even the day was dimming at last. Holding up the glass, Susan drank to bitter endings.

A loud jangling sound intruded on her solitary reverie, like a million bells ringing in her brain. Pressing her fingers tightly against her temples, she listened, wanting to scream at the bells to stop. Did she scream aloud or only inside herself? She wasn't sure. It was the doorbell, she finally decided. Someone was coming over, but she could hardly remember whom, and she didn't want to open the door. Susan stood silently, grasping her glass tightly and waiting for the bells to stop ringing.

All at once, they did stop, and Susan found herself wrapped in a silence as deadly as a shroud. She had to escape. She needed to get out of the house, to go someplace where there were people, light, activity. But there was only one other place for her to go.

The drive was mechanical, she'd made it so many times before. Every street, every turn was automatic, from her front door to the hospital. But once she'd parked her car in the space reserved for staff doctors and pushed through the glass doors, she became conscious of the need to put one foot in front of the other very carefully. It was the only way she could walk down the center of the corridor without veering toward either wall. Usually it was simple enough to go down the hall and take the elevator to the research lab, but suddenly Susan found that even that required her total concentration. In fact, she was so absorbed in getting herself to her destination, that she didn't even see John Dixon when she stepped off the elevator.

"Susan!" he said, catching her arm to break their collision. "What are you doing here? I thought you were sick today."

"Not sick," she corrected. The words

sounded thick and unnatural, so she took great pains to pronounce the next ones clearly. "Indisposed. My ex-husband, Dr. Dan Stewart, a fine physician . . ."

"Susan," John murmured. "You're drunk as a skunk."

"I said," Susan went on with what she was sure was great dignity, "Dr. Dan Stewart, the fine physician, took me to court."

"Over Emily?" he asked, turning away to avoid her breath.

"Exactly." She nodded. "He took her away."

"And you've been drowning your sorrows in Johnnie Walker."

"Un-un." She shook her head. "Dewars."

Dixon groaned. Susan was even drunker than he'd first thought. "Why did you come here?" he asked. "You can't expect to work in your condition."

A strange, pathetic sound, half-hiccup, half-sob, answered him. "Susan, you can't stay here like this," he insisted.

"No place else to go." She swayed so precariously that he took her arm again to keep her from keeling over.

"Come on," he said firmly. "I'm taking you home to sober up. I suppose you're entitled to a drunk today. But if you don't go to bed and sleep it off now, you won't be in any condition to work tomorrow either."

Susan seemed to accept his decision meekly

enough. But the moment John put his arm around her to help her back on the elevator, she collapsed against him. He couldn't help pitying her. She'd staked everything on winning Dan back, and she'd blown it completely.

"What am I going to do?" she sobbed against his shoulder.

"We'll talk about that in the morning," he assured her. He would have promised anything at that moment to calm her. "Right now you need to sleep."

"How can I sleep?" she cried, wishing she had brought the scotch with her to the hospital. It was the only thing that eased the pain. "You don't understand," she sobbed, turning angrily on John. "You don't know what it is to lose someone you love."

For a moment, his grasp tightened around her, the secret fear that he'd been nursing welling up inside him. For a long time, John had thought that Kim was safely his. She'd given up the idea of divorce since his accident, or so it had seemed. But lately, she'd been turning away from him again, avoiding his touch, going to sleep very early or staying up reading until he was safely snoring. He felt as tense as if he were living with a time bomb. At any moment his marriage might blow up in his face, and he didn't know what to do to prevent it. But he couldn't confess all this to Susan. Scared though he was of losing Kim, John couldn't admit it openly. Instead, he steered Susan toward the elevator. The moment of potential self-revelation slipped away.

"I guess you're right," he said, more to himself than to her. "Kim and I have never been happier."

Chapter Eleven
For Better, For Worse

A cool wind was blowing the first leaves off the branches, signaling the changing seasons. All that remained of summer was a memory. For Lisa, it was a very sweet memory, for this summer had been the time when Grant finally obtained his freedom to marry her. She savored it like rare wine.

In less than two hours their wedding bells would chime at last, and she would be Mrs. Grant Coleman for better for worse, for richer for poorer, in sickness and in health. "I do," she murmured to herself with a sigh of supreme contentment, "I do, I do, I do." Although it certainly wasn't her first trip down the aisle, Lisa felt as nervous as any new bride as she pinned her orchid corsage on her shell pink dress and secured her matching pillbox hat. All she had left to put on were the gloves.

Her outfit was simple but elegant, she thought, turning in front of the full-length mirror to admire herself. In fact, everything about her long-awaited wedding to Grant would be simple but elegant. Lisa had planned every detail herself, down to the engraving on the matchbook covers. Now, beaming with satisfaction, she ran through them in her mind. The scene of the wedding was the patio of the Oakdale Country Club. As they arrived, the fifty select guests would be greeted with champagne and lobster pâté and directed into the glass-enclosed sunroom where the ceremony would take place. The reception, immediately following, would spill out onto the patio with more champagne, delicate finger sandwiches, and wedding cake.

A tasteful afternoon wedding for the third —or fourth—time around, Lisa thought. It was expensive without being showy, tasteful without being dull. And Tom had agreed to give her away. In fact, she reminded herself nervously, he should be arriving any second wearing his morning coat, striped pants and top hat. How handsome he'll look, she thought with maternal pride, and Grant . . . Grant will be gorgeous.

Stepping closer to the mirror, Lisa applied her lipstick pencil to the corners of her mouth, studying herself critically as she did. Maybe another touch of powder on her chin?

A dab more perfume behind the ear? Just a tiny, tiny bit more eye shadow to bring out her natural coloring? She didn't want to overdo it—especially for an afternoon wedding—but she wanted to look perfect.

The perfect bride. The perfect wedding. The perfect groom. That was her dream. "And soon, very soon," she said aloud, "it will be a dream come true. Eat your heart out, Joyce!" Lisa said and laughed. "The winner is about to take it all."

Across town in his bachelor apartment, Grant snapped his suspenders angrily. He was dressed and ready to go to the club, ready to take Lisa to be his lawful wedded wife. His bags were packed for their honeymoon and waiting at the door. All he had to do was put on his morning coat and top hat, and get Joyce the hell out of his life.

His dark eyes flashed as he reread the letter that had just arrived special delivery and dialed the number Joyce had added in a scrawled P.S. at the bottom of the page.

As soon as he heard her voice, he lashed out at her without even saying hello. "You have some nerve sending me this outrageous letter on the day—the very hour—that I'm supposed to be getting married!"

For a long moment, there was no response, then a voice oozing with sincerity came through the receiver. "Believe me, Grant, I don't want to spoil anything for you," she insisted.

"Believe me, Grant!" he mocked. "I've been falling for that for how many years? Well this time, Joyce, you've used it once too often. It's not going to work. It's over! You're out of my life!"

"I know you're upset, Grant. It's very human of you, very understandable under the circumstances," Joyce said calmly, as though she were humoring a rebellious child. "But I wrote to you for your own sake. I have nothing to gain by it." She gave a short laugh. "That's not exactly true; I do have an easier conscience now that I've confessed. You can't imagine how many hours I've wrestled with myself about this. Should I tell Grant? Should I go on deceiving him?"

"Cut the acting, Joyce," he interrupted harshly. "The Academy Awards aren't given for another six months."

"Have it our own way, Grant," she said sweetly. "But at least I'm at peace with myself now, knowing that I've done the right thing."

The right thing, he repeated darkly as the receiver went dead in his hand. Joyce had done the right thing, and hung up on him. Now he had to do the right thing and tell Lisa. There wasn't going to be a wedding —not today, not tomorrow. Joyce's story was probably another lie, but if it wasn't. . . .

He had a son. "Grant Coleman, Jr.," he

said the words aloud. A three-year-old boy he'd never seen, never kissed, never carried on his shoulders or tossed up in the air and listened to him laugh.

Sitting down heavily on the edge of the bed, he read Joyce's letter a third time.

Dear Grant,

Believe me when I tell you this is the most difficult letter I will ever have to write. But I will never be able to live at peace with myself until I have confessed the secret that I have been keeping from you for the last three years.

Eight months and one week after you left me, I gave birth to an eight-pound boy. He is a happy, healthy little boy with your deep-set eyes and serious expression. I'm sure you're probably asking yourself why I didn't tell you when I realized I was pregnant. The answer is really very simple—fear. We couldn't talk to each other any longer. Our marriage was on the rocks. I was afraid that you'd insist I get an abortion. After the baby was born, I still couldn't tell you out of fear. For three years I've lived with the fear that you might discover our son and try to take him away from me.

Don't worry, Grant. I left Oakdale to be with him and, now that my conscience is clear, neither of us will come

back to complicate your new life. I wish
you every happiness.

Joyce

Grant crumpled the letter in his fist. When
he walked out on her, Joyce must have been
only a few weeks pregnant, and he'd never
tried to see her again. There had been no
reason to until he needed the divorce to
marry Lisa. Her story could be true. Yet it was
so unlike Joyce to keep the child a secret.
She'd tried so desperately to win him back,
why didn't she ever use their son?

If she'd told him she was pregnant three
years ago, if she'd told him they had a son
even three months ago, Grant thought, how
different their lives might be.

He was still clutching the letter fifteen
minutes later when he burst into Lisa's house.

"Darling!" she cried in surprise when she
saw him. "Don't you know it's bad luck to see
the bride before the wedding?"

"Luck doesn't seem to be on our side
anyway," he mumbled darkly.

"Why? What's the matter, Grant? You
look as if you've been through a war." Lisa
forced herself to speak calmly, but her heart
was racing. Looking intently at Grant, she
saw his troubled eyes, the grim set of his
mouth, and his tightly clenched fist crushing
a ball of paper.

"You'd better sit down, Lisa," he answered.
Although he tried to be gentle, the words

resounded like a curt command. "All the way over here, I've been trying to think of some decent way to break this to you," he began, combing his fingers through his hair. "I can't." He walked several paces away from her, then turned around. "Lisa, I can't go through with the wedding—not now, anyway."

Although she heard Grant's words, she couldn't believe them. "But G—Grant," she stammered, too stunned to think clearly, "I don't understand. It's only minutes away. Our guests . . . the gifts . . ."

"Read this." He pressed the crumpled letter into her hand. "It just came from Joyce."

In a daze, Lisa took the paper, smoothed it out carefully and began to read. Even after she'd finished reading it a second time, it took several minutes before she trusted herself to speak. "Is it true, Grant?" she finally asked.

Closing his eyes, he inhaled sharply. "I don't know, but I have to find out one way or the other. And until I do . . ."

"Oh, Grant!" Lisa cried out, covering her mouth with her hands.

"Lisa, Lisa, darling," he said, taking her in his arms and pressing her against him. "I know it's not fair to even ask you, but can you be patient a little longer. I promise, once this . . . this situation . . . is settled, I'll make it up to you somehow."

"You mean postpone the wedding again?"

she whispered, too devastated even to look at him.

"Just until I find Joyce—and my son," Grant swore.

"Maybe it's for the best." Lisa swallowed hard. "Maybe we just weren't meant to be happy together."

"What do you mean? You're talking nonsense because you're upset." He crushed her in his arms, trying to blot out everything except the warmth of her body, the perfume of her skin. "I won't let Joyce tear us apart. Tell me you'll wait, Lisa, please," Grant urged.

More than anything else in the world, Lisa wanted to be Mrs. Grant Coleman. But her patience was being tested to the breaking point. "I'll try, Grant," she murmured, "but I can't make any more promises . . . not after this."

Susan Stewart felt herself tilting forward, but try though she did, she couldn't regain her balance. "Tired. So tired." She slurred the words so they were unintelligible. The glass beaker she'd been holding slipped from her hand, shattering on the lab floor, and she slumped over the long research table, barely conscious.

At the crash of the beaker, her assistant rushed in. "Please, Dr. Stewart, wake up!" he urged. "Come on, you can't sleep here. What if somebody comes in and sees you? You're already in trouble enough." He sighed in frustration. There was no use wasting his breath. She was too drunk to do anything but sleep it off. If he could just get her into an empty room, he thought, maybe no one would notice her.

Susan had started falling apart the day she lost her daughter. Each day since then she seemed that much worse. At first she came to work with the hint of alcohol on her breath. But lately she'd been stumbling in drunk at the most unpredictable hours and botching all of their experiments. The staff was complaining about the test results it was receiving. The other doctors were avoiding her as if she had a contagious disease, and the nurses were gossiping openly among themselves. Although he felt sorry for her, her assistant was an ambitious young resident, and he was afraid to jeopardize his career.

Sighing in frustration, he tried to wake her up again. Dimly, through the alcoholic haze, Susan heard him calling. But he sounded too far away to answer, and she was so tired. She didn't want to talk. She wanted only to sleep.

Hours later, Susan began to stir. Her throat was parched. Her head felt as big as a balloon. She tried to turn over, but she couldn't seem to move her arms or her legs. In a blind panic she imagined that she was paralyzed. What had happened? Where was she? She opened her eyes, but the light was so blinding she squeezed them shut again.

After a few restless seconds, she squinted one eye open. Someone in a white coat was leaning over her. She was at the hospital, she remembered. She was supposed to be working.

"Are you awake now, Susan?" a familiar voice asked.

"John?" she murmured, trying to focus on him. "It's so bright in here. I can't see. Is it you?"

"I'll close the blinds. That should help," he volunteered.

In a second the room was in shadows. Susan opened her eyes again and looked around her blankly. She was still in the hospital, but she was in a private room, in a hospital bed with the safety guards up. Her arms and legs were constrained as if she were a dangerous patient.

"What am I doing here, tied down like this?" she demanded.

"Looks like you're sleeping off a drunk to me," Dr. Dixon answered sternly. "Another drunk, Susan. You can't keep doing this to yourself."

"But I was working."

"No," he corrected. "You were in the lab, but you weren't working. When you passed out, your assistant tried to get you to a room where you could sleep it off, but you woke up and began raising hell."

She groaned miserably. "Did anybody see me, John?"

He nodded, knowing that there was no point in trying to paint a false picture for her. "Just the entire floor. You woke up and refused to go quietly. In fact, you raised such hell that it took four orderlies to get you in here."

"And the constraints?" she asked bleakly.

"You were thrashing so violently, we had to put them on," he answered. "But I don't think you need them now."

"What I need now is a drink," she said bitterly as he began releasing the ties.

"That's the last thing in the world you need," he scolded. "Can't you see what you're doing? You're throwing away your life, your career, your future."

"I can still work. I'm good at my job," she insisted.

John turned away to evade the issue. He didn't know how to break the news to her. "Dan was in," he said to stall for time.

"Dan?" Susan echoed. "What did he want?"

"To see how you were doing."

"He must have gloated," she muttered bitterly.

"Actually," John corrected, "he seemed genuinely concerned."

"He was just putting on an act for you," Susan said.

For a second, John seemed to hesitate, then

he decided there was no point in putting off the inevitable any longer. "The director was in, too," he said quietly.

"Good grief, what were you doing, John, selling tickets?" Susan screamed.

"He left this letter for you." Ignoring her outburst, he took a white envelope from the bedside table and handed it to her. "I think you should read it now, Susan. I'll wait outside, if you'd rather."

Susan's face paled as he spoke. "It's bad?" she asked, her voice as tentative as a frightened child's.

"I'm afraid so." He nodded grimly.

"Then you read it. Read it aloud to me, John," she begged. Her hand was trembling so she could barely hand him the letter.

"Dear Dr. Stewart," he began in a low somber tone. "It is with the deepest regret that I must request your resignation from the staff of the Memorial Hospital. In spite of the valuable service you have given this hospital in the past, the board of directors feels that you are no longer able to continue your work. It is our sincerest hope that you will seek the necessary treatment for your condition—"

"Just like that?" Susan broke in, too shocked to listen to more. "I'm dismissed! Fired! Kicked out just because I may have been a little drunk?"

"You've been more than a little drunk," John pointed out. "You're turning yourself into an alcoholic. Maybe you already are one," he said bluntly. Though he felt cruel doing it, he knew it was the only way to get her to face the truth about herself.

"Then you're on their side, too," she charged angrily.

"No one is taking sides, Susan," he said as soothingly as he could. "But I certainly agree that you need to get treatment."

Susan sat up too quickly and felt the pain knife through her head. The room was spinning so fast, she didn't dare try to stand up. Instead she sat on the side of the bed crying softly. "I'm not a drunk," she insisted stubbornly. "I've just been upset. I don't know about the rest of you, but I'm human, and I hurt, John, I hurt so much. The only thing that helps is a little drink once in a while."

"It would be one thing if you were only drinking once in a while. But you're drinking every day, and you're not limiting yourself to one drink, either. I'm your friend, Susan, probably one of the few friends you've got left," he said bluntly. "You've got to listen to me."

"You don't know what it's like to lose the only person you've ever loved," she cried. "But maybe when you do, you'll drink too."

Dixon felt himself tense as if all his muscles had suddenly contracted. "We're not talking about me, Susan," he said stiffly. "We're talking about you. Look at yourself in the mirror there. You're a drunk—a pathetic drunk—and you're only going to get worse unless you face the facts."

"A pathetic drunk!" she screamed angrily. "That's what you think I am. Well, you're a blind fool. You don't even know when you've been traded in for a flashier model."

Grasping the edge of the bureau to keep from striking out at her, John demanded in a low, tight voice, "You'd better tell me exactly what you're talking about, Susan."

Too drunk and too angry to be touched by the look of fury in his eyes, she struck back viciously. "I'm talking about your precious Kim and my ex-husband. I caught them together, and believe me, I was cold sober when I did."

John had refused to see the writing on the wall, although it was as clear as a sign printed in giant neon letters. He'd held on to Kim longer than he'd ever dreamed possible. And he'd done it every way he could, by threats, blackmail and deception. He'd played on her pity, manipulated her guilt; he'd done anything to keep her.

But this time, he had lost her. Somehow she'd slipped through his fingers like water. Looking back, John couldn't remember the exact moment when he first realized they were living under the same roof and sharing nothing, that Kim had begun very quietly to step out of his life. None of her day-to-day domestic duties were neglected. His shirts were taken to the laundry, his meals prepared, his bed made without complaint. But that was all. She acted the dutiful wife, but he knew she didn't feel anything for him anymore.

He had married her for her warmth, her vitality, her exuberance, her laughter, her joy—all that she had been denying him. Yet, when he caught her off guard, unaware of his scrutiny, she seemed to sparkle, to shine with a new, secret light he would never control: the glow of love. It made Kim more beautiful than he'd ever known her—and farther from his reach.

Even if he forced her to stay with him, John knew that he would be clinging to an empty shell. The Kim he loved—her heart, her soul, her irrepressible spirit—was gone from him forever. Dan Stewart possessed her now. It should have been obvious to him, John thought, if he had wanted to see. Bright, handsome, vital, Kim and Dan made a movie-screen couple.

There was only one way John Dixon could erase the vision of his wife's silken body wrapped in Dan Stewart's arms. Blinking back the tears that stung his eyes, he put his arm around Susan. He'd been preaching to her for weeks to sober up, but now he was going to eat or, more precisely, drink his words.

"Come on, Susan," he said huskily, "you

and I are going out to get blind, stinking drunk."

She laughed bitterly. "I'm already halfway there, can't you tell?"

"Don't worry," he promised. "I fully intend to catch up with you."

Chapter Twelve
Sons and Lovers

"At least someone in the family is having a wedding," Lisa said with forced gaiety. "I'll drink a toast to that and to your happiness with your new bride, darling." Although she tried not to sound as bleak as she felt, Tom wasn't fooled.

"This means more to me than I can tell you," he said, hugging her tightly. "I mean you being here today in spite of everything, the way you feel about Carol and the mess with Grant. I know what you must be going through."

"Do you, Tom?" she asked vacantly. "Maybe you'll tell me sometime, because I'm not sure I know myself."

"Come on, you know what I'm trying to say," he pleaded. "You and I have never been great about telling each other what we feel."

"I'm sorry, darling, truly I am." Lisa reached up and kissed her son's cheek. "I'm sorry for a lot of things. But I honestly don't know how I'd get through these terribly disappointing days without you to keep my spirits up."

"I just wish there was something I could do for you," Tom said earnestly.

"There is." Lisa gave a brittle laugh. "Get back to your guests and your bride. It isn't fair for a mother to monopolize her son on his wedding day. Anyway, it will make Natalie think she's getting stuck with a domineering mother-in-law."

"Nonsense! You and Natalie are going to be good friends. I told you—"

"I know," Lisa cut in, "more times than I care to remember."

"Maybe I have overdone it a bit, but only because I love you both so much," Tom answered with an assurance he didn't feel. From the first Lisa had seemed so dubious about his second marriage that Tom had never told her about Natalie's letter. Now though he wished he'd confided in his mother. If he hadn't turned it into a dark, bitter secret in his life, maybe he wouldn't still be worrying about it on his wedding day.

Whatever his doubts, Tom had to admit that Natalie made a striking bride. Although her gown was long and white, nothing else about it was traditional. There were no tiers of lace, no wide skirts, no sweeping trains. The dress was absolutely plain, the lines stark and straight, accentuating her own stunning face and figure. Instead of a veil, she wore a single white gardenia pinned in her auburn hair. Tom couldn't help comparing her with Carol. His first bride had floated up the aisle in a cloud of organdy and lace, cheeks flushed, eyes glowing, acting out a little girl's fantasy.

In contrast, Natalie seemed very much a woman, very assured. At least, Tom thought with a trace of sadness, she'll never wake up one morning and find the dream is over because her eyes are already wide open. Natalie knew exactly what she was doing and what she wanted from their marriage. Tom only wished that he knew as well.

Brushing aside the disturbing thoughts, he went over to her side and slipped an arm around her waist as the band began to play. "May I have this dance, Mrs. Hughes," he whispered against her ear.

Natalie turned in his arms, and he felt the quick rush of desire that she always gave him, a sensation of something illicit, something forbidden, something dangerous, explosive. Even though they were now legally man and wife, that hadn't changed, Tom thought with a thrill that both chilled and excited him.

The guests, many of them smiling, a few of them crying, crowded in, forming a circle as they danced. There were one or two in every group who always cried at weddings. Almost all of them were Tom's guests. Natalie had only invited a couple of the women she worked with, saying that she hadn't lived in Oakdale long enough to make many friends. None of her family attended the wedding.

Married in a sea of strangers, Tom thought, wondering how Natalie must feel, but he didn't ask. He'd already learned not to question his new bride too closely. His mother had been right. He didn't really know anything about Natalie. He didn't know where she was coming from, where she wanted to go. He didn't even know if she loved him.

"It's a beautiful wedding, Tom." She was smiling at him, a dazzling smile. "Just what I wanted."

"Happy, then?" He kissed the tip of her nose.

"How could I help it? The wedding is beautiful and so is the groom."

His eyes held hers for a searching moment. "Any regrets, Natalie?"

The smile seemed painted on her lips for the benefit of the wedding guests, yet the trace of a shadow seemed to cross over it. Regrets? Natalie looked over Tom's shoulder at the sea of faces and imagined Luke elbowing his way through the guests, striding onto the dance floor and sweeping her out of her husband's arms. She knew that even now, even on her wedding day she'd go with him.

Nothing had changed except they were both married now. If Luke ever left his wife, she wouldn't hesitate to walk out on Tom.

"Regrets?" She echoed his question with a short laugh. "What would I have to regret, Tom?"

Holding her tighter against him, he inhaled the sweet perfume of her hair. "I don't know." He hesitated. "Marrying me, I guess. Until I saw you walking down the aisle today, I wasn't really sure that you'd show up," he admitted.

Natalie stroked the back of his neck with a manicured finger. "Poor Tom. Were you really afraid I'd leave you standing at the altar?"

"Terrified," he confessed.

"And lose out on this beautiful ring?" she joked, holding up her left hand to admire the platinum circle of diamonds and sapphires that sparkled on her ring finger. "Now tomorrow . . ." She laughed again.

"Tomorrow's too late," he reminded her. "You're mine now, Natalie, for better or worse, and I'm not going to let you forget it."

Tossing back her hair, Natalie gazed up at him, a challenging look in her eyes. "Is that a threat, Mr. Hughes, or a promise?"

"We'll discuss that tonight," he countered with a lusty smile.

"What if I'm one of those women who suddenly lose all interest in sex the moment they get a wedding ring on their finger?"

"You?" He laughed. "It would take a twelve-month freeze to cool you down. That's what's so great about you. You're as hungry as I am."

"Hungrier," Natalie corrected, nipping at his mouth with a kiss that promised to be only the beginning. "Let's get out of here before I embarrass you in front of all your guests."

"We can't leave yet," Tom insisted, even though he very much wanted to be alone with his new bride. "The reception just began."

"You can make an excuse," Natalie said. "Tell them the excitement has been too much for me."

"You're shameless." He laughed huskily.

"Mmmm," she breathed into his ear. "I am, and you love it. Now are you going to make up some lie, or am I going to tell them the truth."

Watching the newlyweds dance, the guests murmured among themselves what a happy, wholesome couple Tom and Natalie made. Only one person watched them dance with grave misgivings. Although she knew it was wishful thinking, Lisa had hoped up until the last moment that somehow Tom and Carol would get back together. Now studying Natalie, she felt a wave of apprehension wash over her.

Tom was wrong, Lisa thought. She and Natalie would never be friends. But they could easily become bitter enemies. The girl was stunning and poised—and devious. Lisa could see it in her eyes, hear the false note in her laugh. Crossing her fingers, she prayed that Tom would be happy with his new bride. But even as she did, every instinct warned her that her son had made the worst mistake of his life.

Closing the door behind her with infinite care, Kim slipped out of the marriage that had imprisoned her body and soul. Somewhere upstairs, probably in their bedroom window, she knew John was watching her go. But she wouldn't look up. In fact she didn't want to look back any more than she wanted to remember her husband with bitterness.

John had always loved her, Kim had never doubted that. But she had married him for all the wrong reasons and stayed with him long after she should have left. She didn't blame him any more than she blamed herself. Their marriage had been a mistake, and she wanted it to end without guilt or recriminations. Surprisingly, this time when she told John she was leaving, he had accepted the inevitable without a battle. It was almost as though he had been waiting for her to go. It was a strangely haunting feeling, Kim thought as she tiptoed out.

From the upstairs window John watched for her to appear in the driveway. The cars, the trees, the landscape dissolved in a blur of tears. In the last few weeks, the strain had been so great that when Kim finally said good-bye, his sense of relief had outweighed his loss. Even then, he didn't admit that he knew about Dan Stewart. He didn't tell her that every time he looked at her now, he imagined her in Dan's arms and when he tried to sleep, he dreamed of them making love.

Sliding her valise into the backseat, Kim got in the car and turned on the ignition. Another day, when John was at the hospital, she would come back to collect the rest of her things. She didn't want to take anything from their marriage except her clothes and personal things. She wanted to be free of everything —even memories. Free to begin living and loving again.

Dan would be waiting for her at his office, waiting to take her home to meet Betsy. The little girl had never known a mother, but Kim hoped that would change very soon. She wanted to be a mother to Emily too. Poor little Emily! Kim hoped the child would accept her and let her heal the wounds she'd suffered with Susan.

And poor Susan! No one had come out of that tragedy unscathed. Kim felt a surge of pity for the woman. Her only motivation had been love, a desperate, misguided love for Dan. How could Kim condemn her now that she also knew what it meant to love Dan Stewart. It was an all-powerful, all-consuming passion that eclipsed every other feeling, every other commitment. What would she do if Dan ever left her for another woman? Kim shuddered at the thought.

Laughing to herself, she pulled up short at a red light. She was already planning a life for them and Dan hadn't even proposed marriage. They'd never even talked about it, yet it seemed as inevitable as the sun rising in the morning. The two of them were meant for each other. Now that their lives had touched so intimately, she couldn't imagine living without him.

Until she was actually free of John, Kim had never allowed herself to look ahead beyond the next day, the next clandestine meeting with Dan. Now her dreams came thick and fast. Driving faster than she should, Kim tried to imagine what it would be like to have a ready-made family: a husband she adored and two daughters, one seven and one four. But even as she imagined the four of them together, more attractive, steamy dreams intruded.

As long as she'd lived with John, Kim couldn't bring herself to make love to Dan. What they felt for each other was too special, too important to rush in a stolen hour. When she gave herself to him, she wanted to surrender openly, totally. Now she could.

The road signs sped by in a blur as her foot pressed harder on the gas. But it was a late Sunday morning and the traffic was light. In a few more minutes she would be with her love, Kim thought. Her cheeks flushed as she felt a rush of desire surge through her body. Was Dan as eager to know her at last?

Kim tried to concentrate on the road instead of the man who was waiting at the end of it, but her heart was pounding when she finally pulled up behind his car and hurried up the walk to his office door. A brass plate engraved with his name was fastened over the bell. Kim reached out to press it, but before she could, the door flew open.

She didn't have to dream anymore, or yearn, or imagine, or wonder, because Dan was standing just inches away. All she had to do was reach out and claim him.

"Are you all right, sweetheart?" he asked, sweeping her into his arms.

"Now I am," she answered, filled with contentment, joy, and tremulous excitement.

"I thought you'd never get here." He shuddered with a deep feeling of relief.

"That's funny," Kim murmured against his cheek. "I must have broken every speed limit."

Pressing her close against him, Dan planted a single kiss in the sensitive hollow of her throat. "I guess I was afraid that you'd get cold feet at the last minute and decide to stay with John," he confessed.

Kim looked up at him, suddenly very serious. "I didn't leave John for you, Dan, not really," she admitted. "Loving you just gave me the courage to do something that I should have done a long, long time ago."

"Maybe so." He gave her a rueful smile. "But I'm glad you waited to come to me. I want to take you home with me, to meet the girls, but not yet. Right now, for a little while anyway, I want to keep you all to myself."

"What exactly do you plan to do with me, Doctor?" She laughed happily.

"What I've wanted to do ever since I stole a kiss in the middle of your kitchen. It seems like so long ago now, doesn't it? The cocktail party you and John gave to welcome me back to Oakdale. I never had such a tempting hostess before."

"And I never had such an irresistible guest of honor."

"I thought you were just being polite when you let me kiss you."

"Not exactly," Kim admitted.

"Then come inside with me," Dan said, "and you can tell me exactly what you had in mind."

"I thought you'd never ask." Kim breathed each word against his lips.

"I've been waiting for the perfect moment," he said, sliding his hands down the small of her back.

"Don't you know that you can wait forever? The perfect moment never comes." She shivered with delightful anticipation at his touch.

"But this time it did," he whispered, brushing the corners of her mouth with kisses.

Kim gazed up at him with eyes as bright as sunlight. "I feel as if I've been waiting my whole life for you, Dan."

"Then I'm not going to keep you waiting any longer." Although his words were teasing, the huskiness of his voice betrayed the depth of his desire. Taking her hand, he led her into the examining room and closed the door.

Moving like a dancer to a music only she could hear, Kim rushed into Dan's embrace. Locked in his arms, she knew it was just a beginning. Their love was so complete, it set them free of all constraints. So much lay ahead of them, so many possibilities, so many glorious tomorrows waiting for their love.

The last thing John Dixon needed was a visit from Susan Stewart. He had lost Kim, he had no doubt of that now. Yet Susan's persistent knocking forced him to admit her to his home.

"Don't start with me, Susan," he warned her as he flung open the door and strided toward the bar. "I've had a bad day and I'd like to keep it from getting any worse."

Undaunted, Susan swung John around by the arm and forced him to face her. "You're just going to give up. That's it, isn't it? You're a fraud! You never really loved Kim at all!"

John bristled at Susan's stinging words. "Get out of here or I swear—"

Susan's bitter laugh stopped John from continuing. "So you do love her," she said gently. John's silence was enough of an answer for both of them. "They're laughing at us, you know." Susan knew that would get to John; he couldn't stand the thought of Dan Stewart mocking him. After studying his response a moment longer, Susan decided to play her trump card. "You can give up if you want to." She moved slowly toward the door. "*I'm* not. I love Dan too much to give him up. I intend to fight for him." Susan held her breath as she reached the door, solemnly hoping that John would stop her from leaving. She was not disappointed.

"Susan, wait." John's voice was urgent. "Maybe there's a way—I think I know how we can keep Dan and Kim apart."

Susan turned to face him, her lips curved in a cunning smile. "I'm all ears, John."

How to Win Big Prizes

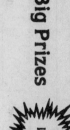